P.O. Box 1375
Barrhead
Glasgow
G78 1JJ

Tel: 0141 880 6839

Fax: 0870 124 9189

e-mail: teejaypublishers@btinternet.com

web page: www.teejaypublishers.co.ok

Level 3b Textbook

Produced by members of the TeeJay Writing Group

T Strang, J Geddes and J Cairns.

PUPIL BOOK

3b

Level 3b Textbook

The book, along with CfE Book 3a can be used in both upper Primary and Secondary 1/2 with pupils who have successfully completed CfE Level 2 and who are likely to be following the National 5 course in S3 or earlier.

- Those pupils going onto a national 5 course should complete the contents of books 3a and 3b by the end of Secondary 2, some earlier and some later.

- As a guide, Book 3b might be started with most pupils at the beginning of, or part way through S2.

- There are no A and B exercises. The 2 books cover the entire Level 3 CfE course without the teacher having to pick and choose which questions to leave out and which exercises are important. They all are !

- Pupils who cope well with the contents of Level 3 may be able to begin work on National 5 during S2.

- The book contains a 7 page "Chapter Zero", which primarily revises all those strands from CfE Level 3 that have been covered in Book 3a.

- Topics which have been completed in Book 3a, are reintroduced as *Review Exercises* in Book 3b, to help consolidate and revise the topics in preparation for National 5.

- Each chapter will have a "Revisit - Review - Revise" exercise as a summary.

- Chapter 14 revises every strand of Level 3 in preparation for TeeJay's Level 3 Diagnostic Assessment.

- Teachers are encouraged, at the end of various chapters, to consider assessing the pupils using the corresponding TeeJay Outcome Assessment.

- Homework* is available as a photocopiable pack.

- TeeJay's Assessment Pack* for each Level, early to 3, is available and can be used topic by topic or combined to form a series of Level 3 cumulative Tests.

  We make no apologies for the multiplicity of colours used throughout the book, both for text and in diagrams - we feel it helps brighten up the pages !!

T Strang, J Geddes, J Cairns

(August 2012)

* Available for purchase separately.

Index

Book 3(b)

* Topics listed with a star have been brought forward from Level 4 - We believe they lie better in Level 3.

The brown *(Review)* exercises provide revision of the topics met in Book 3(a)

CHAPTER 0

Before continuing the CfE Level 3 course using Book 3b, this chapter will give you a chance to revise those topics at Level 3, already covered in Book 3a.

Each topic will also be covered in depth in one of the interspersed *Review Exercises*.

Calculators should NOT be used unless the symbol appears.

Rounding

1. Round each of the following to 1 significant figure :-   a   3501   b   247 800.

2. Round each of the following to 2 significant figures :-   a   67 845   b   0·9875.

3. Round each of the following to 3 significant figures :-   a   126 903   b   0·06218.

4. How many significant figures have each of the following numbers been rounded to ?

    a   0·0507   b   0·0090   c   20 003.

5. Round each number to **one significant figure** then give an **approximate** answer to each :-

    a   412 x 38   b   2137 x 384   c   0·229 x 296

    d   5824 ÷ 19   e   879 300 ÷ 3115   f   0·3732 ÷ 1·83.

6. Rounded to 1 significant figure, the number of people at a concert was 8000.

    What was the greatest number of people who could have been at the concert ?

Whole Numbers

7. Calculate :-

    a   31 x 30   b   423 x 2000   c   403 x 400

    d   6600 ÷ 30   e   800 000 ÷ 400   f   84 000 ÷ 60.

8. Carefully, work out the answers to the following :-

    a   20 - 5 x 2   b   16 - 8 ÷ 2 + 5   c   20 ÷ (2 + 3).

9. Re-write the following and insert brackets to make each of the statements correct :-

    a   7 + 2 x 4 = 36   b   15 ÷ 5 - 2 = 5   c   7 + 8 ÷ 2 + 3 = 3.

10. A group of 8 people, a mixture of adults and children, bought tickets for the London Eye.

    The bill came to £97·20.

    How many adults and how many children must there have been ?

London Eye Ticket Price	
Adult	£18·90
Child	£9·90

11. What is the :- a supplement of 75° b complement of 75° ?

12. Copy and complete each diagram below, filling in **all** missing angles :-

a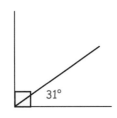

b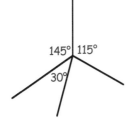

c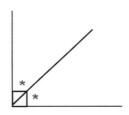

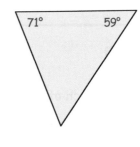

d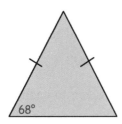

e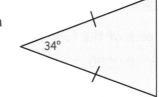

f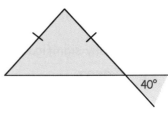

g

h

i

13. Find :-

  a 8 – 11   b –8 + 10   c 13 + (–6)   d 7 – (–3)

  e –5 – (–2)   f –15 – (–25)   g –3 + (–6) – (–9)   h –20 – (–9) – (–8).

14. Find :-

  a –2 + 3 – (–4) + (–5)   b 18 – (–10) + (–19) – 8   c 65 + (–72) – (–45).

15. Find :-

  a 5 × (–4)   b (–7) × (–3)   c 20 ÷ (–4)   d (–24) ÷ (–6)

  e 3 × (–6) × 2   f (–5) × (–3) × (–1)   g (–86) × (–29) × 0   h (–80) ÷ (–5) × (–3)

  i 5 × (–1) × (–3)   j –3 × (–8) + (–4) ÷ (–2).

16. a

From the entrance to a cave to the back of the cave, the temperature dropped from 12°C down to -13°C.

By how much had the temperature dropped ?

  b A small submarine was at a depth of -85 metres. It rose by 30 metres before descending 105 metres to the ocean floor.

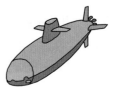

What was the depth of the ocean at that point ?

17. From the coordinate diagram :-

    a   Write down the coordinates of all the points.

    b   Which 2 points have the same x coordinate ?

    c   Which points have the same x and y coordinate ?

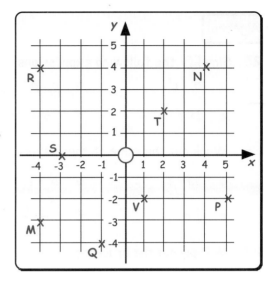

18. Draw a set of axes (-4 to 4 on both scales).

    a   Plot the points A(-1, 0), B(-3, 4) and C(1, 2).

    b   Plot a 4th point (D) so that figure ABCD is a
        rhombus and write down the coordinates of D.

    c   Reflect figure ABCD in the x-axis, showing its new position in your diagram,
        (A'B'C'D'), and write down the coordinates of A', B', C' and D'.

Fractions, Decimals & Percentages

19. Change each percentage to a **decimal** and then to a **fraction** in its simplest form :-

    a   20%   b   5%   c   36%   d   75%   e $66\frac{2}{3}$%   f $\frac{1}{2}$% .

20. Change each of the following into a **percentage** :-

    a   0·35   b   0·04   c $\frac{7}{10}$ d $\frac{11}{40}$ e   1·5   f $\frac{1}{3}$.

21. Find :-

    a $\frac{3}{5}$ of £80   b   2% of £1200   c   75% of £4000   d   0·3 of $4000.

22. Sandy bought an electric guitar for £240.
    He sold it later to a friend for **25% less** than what he bought it for.

    For how much did Sandy sell his guitar ?

23. Find :-

    a   17% of £340   b $\frac{5}{8}$ of 992 kg   c   0·65 of £16·40   d $37\frac{1}{2}$ % of £176

    e $\frac{11}{15}$ of €6450   f $\frac{1}{2}$ % of £840   g $12\frac{1}{2}$ % of $\frac{3}{5}$ of £12 000.

24. a

Sally's monthly pay last year as a beautician was £1850.

This year she received a **pay rise** of 3·5%.

What is Sally's new :-   (i)   monthly pay   (ii)   annual salary ?

    b   Farmer Giles buys food supplement for his sheep. A sack usually feeds
        60 sheep but this month the sack contains an **extra 30%** feeding.

        How many sheep will a sack now feed ?

25. Simplify the following expressions :-

   a $d + d$ b $p \times p$ c $4c \times 8$ d $7x + 5y - 2x - y$

   e $t \times t \times t$ f $5b^2 \times 7ab$ g $15m^2 \div 3m$ h $60n^2 \div 5n.$

26. Work out the value of these expressions when $a = 5$, $b = 4$ and $c = -2$:-

   a $3a + b$ b $b^2 + c^2$ c abc d $3b^2$

   e $\sqrt{b}$ f $\dfrac{2a + c}{b}$ g $\dfrac{4a}{b + c}$ h $\sqrt{3b - 2c}.$

27. Multiply out the brackets :-

   a $5(x + 3y)$ b $3m(m - 5)$ c $-4(h - 3)$ d $-2q(5 - q).$

28. Expand the brackets and then **simplify** :-

   a $5(x + 2) - 10$ b $8b + 4(b - 3)$ c $2 + 3(d - 2)$

   d $12 + 6(2x - 3)$ e $2(3t - 1) - 5(t - 1)$ f $3g - (4 - g).$

29. For each of the following formula, work out the value of the capital letter :-

   a $T = 2d + e.$ Find T, when $d = 6.5$ and $e = 0.4$.

   b $W = \sqrt{a + bc}$. Find W, when $a = 11$, $b = 2.5$ and $c = 10$.

30.

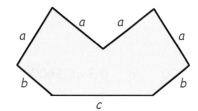

   a   Construct a formula for finding P, the perimeter of the shape shown opposite.

   b   Find P, when $a = 10$, $b = 7$ and $c = 13$.

   c   Find c, when $P = 81$, $a = 12$ and $b = 9$.

Area & Perimeter

31. Calculate the area of each of these :-

a
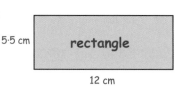
rectangle

c
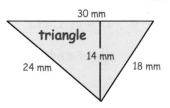

d
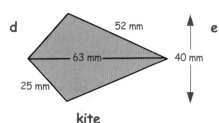
kite

e

f
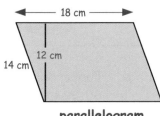
parallelogram

32. Calculate the **perimeter** of each of the shapes in **Question 31**.

33. Calculate the **area** of these shapes, showing each step of your working :-

a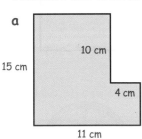

b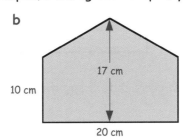

c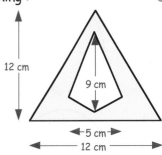

Fraction Work

34. Write two equivalent fractions for :-   a $\frac{1}{5}$ b $\frac{3}{11}$.

35. Find and **simplify** where possible :-

a $\frac{5}{8} + \frac{1}{8}$ b $\frac{1}{3} + \frac{1}{4}$ c $\frac{4}{5} + \frac{1}{3}$ d $\frac{3}{5} + \frac{2}{3} - \frac{1}{2}$.

36. Change to a **top heavy fraction** :-   a $2\frac{1}{5}$ b $4\frac{5}{6}$.

37. Change to a **mixed number** :-   a $\frac{7}{6}$ b $\frac{28}{5}$.

38. Find each of the following, leaving your answer as a **mixed number** :-

a $3\frac{2}{5} + 4\frac{2}{5}$ b $5\frac{7}{8} - 1\frac{1}{8}$ c $1\frac{1}{4} + 2\frac{2}{3}$ d $10\frac{7}{8} - 7\frac{1}{4}$

e $6\frac{3}{4} - 2\frac{2}{5}$ f $5\frac{1}{4} - 1\frac{1}{3}$ g $8\frac{2}{5} - 5\frac{5}{6}$ h $7 - 2\frac{3}{8}$.

39. I began with $4\frac{3}{4}$ litres of Irn Bru. During the evening I drank $2\frac{1}{3}$ litres.

How much Irn Bru was I left with ?

Circle Work   *Give all answers correct to 3 significant figures.*

40. Calculate the **circumference** of each of these :-

a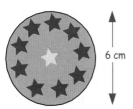

b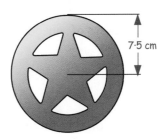

41. Calculate the **diameter** of a dinner plate with a **circumference** of 37·68 inches.

42. Work out the **radius** of this circular drain cover
which has a **circumference** of 188·4 centimetres

$C = 188·4$ cm

43. Calculate the **perimeter** of each shape : -

a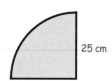

25 cm

b

15 mm

9 mm

c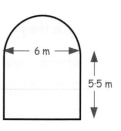

6 m

5·5 m

44. Find the **area** of each object below correct to **3 significant figures** : -

a

spinner radius = 35 mm

b

orange radius = 4·25 cm

c

clock diameter = 1·8 m

45. Find the **area** of each of these shapes correct to **3 significant figures** : -

a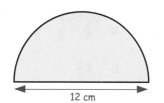

12 cm

b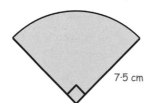

7·5 cm

c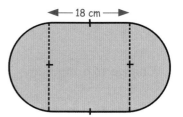

18 cm

Ratio

46. Of the 45p change in my pocket, 27p was made up of coppers.

Write down the ratio of :- copper coins : silver coins and **simplify** this ratio.

47. Simplify the following ratios as far as possible :-

a   12 : 18   b   44 : 33   c   25 : 75   d   42 : 56

e   26 : 39   f   17 : 19   g   5 : 7·5   h   1250 : 750.

48. The ratio of apple trees : pear trees in an orchard is 3 : 5.

There are 24 apple trees. How many pear trees are there ?

49. Danny bought packets of plain and vinegar crisps. The ratio of plain : vinegar was 5 : 4.

There were 20 packets of vinegar crisps. How many packets of crisps were there **altogether** ?

Volume

50. Calculate the **volume** of this tin of biscuits.   16 cm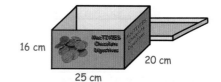

20 cm

25 cm

51.

The **volume** of this carton of apple juice is 1000 cm³.

Calculate the **height** of the carton.

10 cm   8 cm

52. Change to litres :- a 3500 ml   b 200 ml   c 30 ml.

53. Change to ml :- a $2\frac{1}{2}$ litres   b 3·15 litres   c $\frac{4}{5}$ litre.

54. Find the **volume** of each of these shapes :-

a

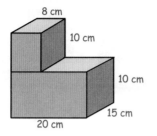

8 cm
10 cm
10 cm
15 cm
20 cm

b

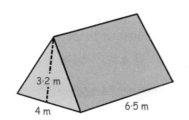

3·2 m
4 m
6·5 m

55. This plastic cold water storage tank is a cuboid and it measures 1·8 m by 1·2 m by 80 centimetres deep.

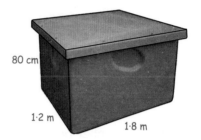

80 cm
1·2 m
1·8 m

a Calculate the volume of the storage tank in cm³.

b How many litres of water will it hold when full ?

Time - Distance - Speed

56. a How far will a ship travel in 4 hours at an average speed of 15 km per hour ?

b How long will it take me to drive 200 miles at an average speed of 40 miles per hour ?

c What is the average speed of a plane which covered 1050 miles in 3 hours ?

57. Calculate :-

a the total distance covered by a train, going at an average speed of 80 mph for 2 hours and 30 minutes.

b the average speed of a bus which took 3 hours 15 minutes to travel 130 miles.

c the time taken by a ship to travel 126 kilometres at an average speed of 24 km/hr.

58. A pilot flew his light airplane from Barton Airport to Cranfoot airport, picked up a passenger and flew back to Barton again.

The graph shows his journey.

a When did he reach Cranfoot ?

b How long did he spend there ?

c Calculate his average speed for the journey from Barton to Cranfoot.

d On the way back, he met a "head wind". Did this slow him down or help him ? (*Explain why, using the graph*).

e Calculate his speed for the return leg of his trip.

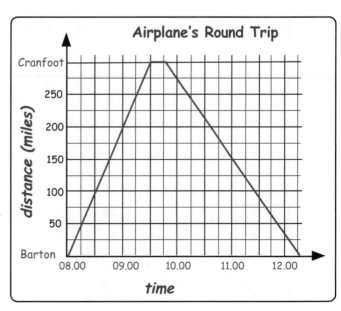

Airplane's Round Trip

Cranfoot
250
200
150
100
50
Barton

distance (miles)

08.00 09.00 10.00 11.00 12.00

time

CHAPTER 1

Powers and Roots

Squares, Cubes and Powers (Indices)

Be able to square & cube numbers and also raise them to a power

4^2

2^3

- To square a number means to multiply it by itself.

  e.g. the "square" of 4 is .. $4 \times 4 = 16$ (not 4×2).

  This is shortened to "4 squared = $4 \times 4 = 16$",
  or better still $4^2 = 4 \times 4 = 16$. (4^2 is read as four squared).

- To cube a number means to multiply it by itself, then itself again.

  e.g. the "cube" of 2 is $2 \times 2 \times 2 = 8$ (not 2×3).
  This is shortened to "2 cubed = $2 \times 2 \times 2 = 8$", or better still $2^3 = 2 \times 2 \times 2 = 8$.
  (2^3 is read as "two cubed")

The smaller number on the right shoulder is known as an index (plural "indices") or a power.

Example :- 3^5 (read as 3 to the power of 5) = $3 \times 3 \times 3 \times 3 \times 3 = 243$.

Exercise 1

1. Do not use a calculator in this question. Copy and complete the following. :-

   a $3^2 = 3 \times 3 = \ldots$ b $5^2 = 5 \times 5 = \ldots$ c $6^2 = 6 \times \ldots = \ldots$

   d $8^2 = \ldots \times \ldots = \ldots$ e $7^2 =$ f $9^2 =$

   g $10^2 =$ h $1^2 =$ i $20^2 =$

   j $(-1)^2 =$ k $(-8)^2 =$ l $(\frac{1}{2})^2 =$

   m $4^3 = 4 \times 4 \times 4 = \ldots$ n $3^3 = 3 \times 3 \times \ldots = \ldots$ o $5^3 = \ldots \times \ldots \times \ldots = \ldots$

   p $6^3 = \ldots \times \ldots = \ldots$ q $1^3 =$ r $10^3 =$

   s $(-1)^3 =$ t $(-2)^2 =$ u $(\frac{1}{2})^3 =$

   v $2^4 =$ w $3^6 =$ x $4^5 = .$

2. You can use a calculator this time. Find the value of :-

   a 13^2 b 17^2 c 21^2 d 26^2

   e 37^2 f 100^2 g 19^2 h 300^2

   i 29^2 j 51^2 k 43^2 l 58^2

   m 8^3 n 12^3 o 19^3 p 25^3

   q $(-9)^3$ r $(\frac{1}{7})^3$ s 6^4 t 7^7

   u 2^8 v 3^{10} w 10^6 x 20^5.

3. You can calculate the **area** of a **square** using the formula :-

$$Area = (length)^2$$

or $A = L^2$

Use this formula to calculate the areas of the following squares :-

a 9·5 cm

Area = L^2
=> A = $9·5^2$
A = ... cm^2

b 18 cm

Area = L^2
=> A = 18^2
A = ... cm^2

c 27 cm

Area = L^2
=> A = ...^{2}
A = ... cm^2

d 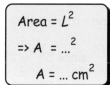 12·2 cm

Area = L^2
=> A = ...^{2}
A = ... cm^2

4. Use your calculator to find :-

a $4^2 + 5^2$ b $9^2 + 8^2$ c $10^2 + 7^2$ d $9^2 + 2^2$

e $13^2 + 12^2$ f $2^2 + 3^2 + 5^2$ g $10^2 + 8^2 + 6^2$ h $20^2 + 21^2$.

5. a Use your calculator to find each of the following :-

$1^2 - 0^2$, $2^2 - 1^2$, $3^2 - 2^2$, $4^2 - 3^2$, $5^2 - 4^2$, $6^2 - 5^2$, $7^2 - 6^2$.

b Did you notice a pattern ? If so, write down the value of $8^2 - 7^2$ without using your calculator. Now check your guess with a calculator.

c No calculator. Write down the value of :- $9^2 - 8^2$, $20^2 - 19^2$, $101^2 - 100^2$.

6. Optional — (only if you have a **scientific calculator**).

If you have a scientific calculator, it will have a button like this ....

$\boxed{x^y}$ or $\boxed{y^x}$. This is useful for finding powers of a number.

a Find 5^8 by writing it as 5 x 5 x 5 x 5 x 5 x 5 x 5 x 5 and working it out.

b To find 5^8, using the $\boxed{x^y}$ do the following :- Press $\boxed{5}$ $\boxed{x^y}$ $\boxed{8}$ $\boxed{=}$

You should get the same answer as in part a, but a lot quicker !

7. Use a scientific calculator to find :-

a 4^4 b 6^5 c 10^5 d 8^6 e 9^3 f 3^7

g 6^8 h 7^4 i 1^{23} j 0^8 k 2^7 l 11^4

m 3^9 n 5^{12} o 100^4 p 10^{10} q $(-2)^4$ r $(-5)^5$.

Be able to find the square root of any number and some simple cube roots

Square Root

You already know how to find "six squared" $6^2 = 6 \times 6 = 36$.

We can reverse this process by asking "what number, times itself, gives 36" ?

From above, you can see that the answer must be 6.

We say that "the square root of 36 is 6", which shortens to $\boxed{\sqrt{36} = 6}$

Exercise 2

1. Copy each line and complete :-

   a since $3^2 = 9 \Rightarrow \sqrt{9} = 3$

   b since $5^2 = 25 \Rightarrow \sqrt{25} = ..$

   c since $7^2 = 49 \Rightarrow \sqrt{49} = ..$

   d since $8^2 = 64 \Rightarrow \sqrt{64} = ...$

   e since $9^2 = ? \Rightarrow \sqrt{?} = ...$

   f since $10^2 = ? \Rightarrow \sqrt{?} = ...$

2. Write down the answer to each of the following :-

   a $\sqrt{16}$ b $\sqrt{1}$ c $\sqrt{400}$ d $\sqrt{900}$.

3. You can now use the "$\sqrt{}$" button on your calculator to find :-

   a $\sqrt{400}$ b $\sqrt{900}$ c $\sqrt{121}$ d $\sqrt{361}$ e $\sqrt{225}$

   f $\sqrt{256}$ g $\sqrt{169}$ h $\sqrt{289}$ i $\sqrt{1.44}$ j $\sqrt{20.25}$.

> Most square roots are not exact :- $\sqrt{19} = 4.358898944 = 4.36$ (to 2 decimal places)

4. Use your calculator to find the following to two decimal places :-

   a $\sqrt{17}$ b $\sqrt{26}$ c $\sqrt{34}$ d $\sqrt{71}$ e $\sqrt{95}$

   f $\sqrt{109}$ g $\sqrt{186}$ h $\sqrt{600}$ i $\sqrt{750}$ j $\sqrt{1000}$.

5. The square shown has an area of 324 mm^2.

   Calculate the length of one of its sides.

324 mm^2

Cube Root

At this stage, we will look only at simple examples.

As "two cubed" $2^3 = 2 \times 2 \times 2 = 8$, then the "cube root" of 8 is 2. $\boxed{\sqrt[3]{8} = 2}$

   i.e. "what number $\times$ itself, $\times$ itself again gives 8" ?

6. The answers to these questions are all whole numbers. Find :-

   a $\sqrt[3]{27}$ b $\sqrt[3]{64}$ c $\sqrt[3]{125}$ d $\sqrt[3]{1000}$ e $\sqrt[3]{1000000}$.

1. Find the **area** of the square shown.

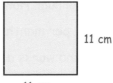

11 cm

11 cm

2. Find the **area** of a square with side :-

   a   9 mm
   b   30 cm
   c   0·5 m.

3. Find :-

   a 5^2
   b 8^2
   c 10^2
   d 15^2
   e 100^2
   f 40^2.

4. Find :-

   a 2^3
   b 2^4
   c 10^4
   d 3^4
   e 10^6
   f 1^{29}.

5. Find :-

   a $\sqrt{49}$
   b $\sqrt{81}$
   c $\sqrt{0}$
   d $\sqrt{144}$
   e $\sqrt{169}$
   f $\sqrt{2500}$.

You may use a calculator for questions 6 to 9.

6. Calculate the **area** of a square with side :-

   a   33 cm
   b   2·6 mm
   c   85 m.

7. Find :-

   a 17^2
   b $5·1^2$
   c $3·14^2$
   d 6^5
   e 13^6
   f $6·3^4$.

8. Find the following and write your answers to **3 significant figures.**

   a $\sqrt{23}$
   b $\sqrt{204}$
   c $\sqrt{0·75}$.

9. This square lawn has an **area** of 42 square metres.

   Find the length of a side of the lawn to **2 decimal places.**

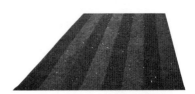

REVIEW 1

1. a   Lucy earns £345·50 per week. How much does she earn in a year ?

    b   Derek's salary is £29 640 per annum. How much is his monthly pay ?

    c   Gary is paid a salary of £2420 per month. What is his annual salary ?

    d   Louise earns £11·60 per hour and works a 35 hour week.

        How much does she earn in a year ?

2. Baz works for a tyre repair company. He is paid £12·40 per hour.

    a   How much will he earn in a week if he works for 40 hours ?

    Last week Baz also worked 8 hours overtime, at time and a half.

    b   Calculate how much he earned for his overtime.

    c   What was Baz's total pay for last week ?

3. a    Jenny's gross pay last year, as a designer, was £32 524.

        Her net pay was £26 845.

        What were her total deductions last year ?

    b   Steve works as a school janitor and his
        net income this year was £21 944.

        His deductions came to £4655.

        Calculate Steve's gross annual income.

4. Cheryl has a gross income of £3085 per month.

    She pays £175·50 in National Insurance, £89·75 in Graduated
    Pension and her Income Tax is 15% of her gross pay.

    a   How much are Cheryl's total deductions ?

    b   What is her net income ?

5. Look at Millie's torn payslip for May 2012.

    Calculate what Millie's Income Tax was.

Name :- Millie Pede		Month :- May 201
Gross Pay for Month :-		**Deductions for Month :-**
Basic	£1764·25	Income Tax £
Overtime	£183·70	National Insurance £85·45
Bonus	£45·00	Graduated Pension £63·60
Total Gross		
		Total Net Pay £1546·40

6. The average gross annual income for 2012 in Scotland was £26 500.

    The average total deductions were estimated at 22% of the gross income.

    a   Calculate what the average person paid in deductions in 2012.

    b   Calculate what the average net monthly pay was in Scotland in 2012.

CHAPTER 2

Foreign Exchange - Revisited

Be able to use money exchange in a foreign currency

Remember - many countries use different currencies.

Shown are the currency exchange rates for various countries.

British Pound (July 2012)	£1 =
Euro	1·24
American Dollar ($)	1·55
Chinese Yen	9·83
Indian Rupee	85·56
Mexican Peso	21·70
Norwegian Krone	9·40
South African Rand	13·03

Correct as of July 2012.

Example 1 :-

How many Euros will I get for £250 ?

$$250 \times 1·24 = 310 €$$

*To change from £'s to another currency - multiply.

Example 2 :-

How many £(GBP) will I get for $285·20 ?

$$285·20 \div 1·55 = £184$$

*To change from another currency back to £'s - divide.

Exercise 1

Use the exchange rates given in the table above to answer the following questions :-

1. Len has £450 to spend on holiday. Change his spending money into :-

   a Euros   b Yen   c Rand   d Rupee.

2. Alice has a balance of £1220 in her bank account.

   Change her bank account balance into each of the foreign currencies in question 1.

   Scotia Bank
   2311 3234 5898 0041
   Valid from 02/12   Expires 02/14
   Alice Johnson
   Sortcode 200347   Acc No. 00176502

3. Change each of the following into Euros :-

   a   b   c    d

   £12·50   £980   £2600   £24 600

4. Change each of the following into GBP (Great British Pounds) to the nearest penny :-

   a $1200   b 75 390 Rupees   c 3000 Pesos   d 225 000 Krone.

5. Ellen bought her laptop in Hamburg, Germany for 542 €.
   Kara bought the same laptop in San Francisco, America for $642.
   Louise had paid £442 in Edinburgh for the identical laptop.

   Who got the best deal ? *Explain.*

6. Which is the best deal for each of the following :–

a

€322 $370

b

3909   3440·50   7486·50
Rand   Yen   Peso's

7. a Agnes took £760 spending money to France.
     She spent €740 on her holiday.

     How many GBP did she return home with ?

   b Jessie took £1250 spending money to Paris.
     She spent €650 on her hotel and €540 on food.

     Does she have enough for a €260 trip to EuroDisney ?

8. 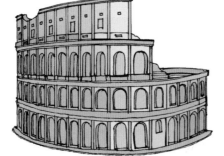 Kevin took £960 on holiday to Italy.
   He spent 90% of his money.

   How many Euros did he have left ?

9. Sara also went on holiday to Italy.
   She returned home with £200 which
   was 25% of her original spending money.

   How many Euros did she spend on holiday ?

10. Mr Forbes was given a £850 expenses account.
    He changed this into Euros and spent €700 in Italy.
    He then went to India and spent 1670 Rupees, and on
    to America where he spent $450.

    Did Mr Forbes overspend on his expense account ? Explain.

11. a Change €600 into GBP. Now change this amount into American dollars.

    b Describe how you would change Rand into Yen.

    c Change 2606 Rand into Yen.

12. Use the currency exchange rate to convert :–

    a $3100 into euros   b €620 into Yen   c 470 krone into Rupees.

13. Mr Lee took his £20000 savings and went on a trip round the world.

    He spent 18000 Rupees in India, 12800 Rand in South Africa,
    €7500 in France and $11000 in the USA.

    How much, in £'s did he have left, to the nearest £10, when his trip ended ?

Best Buys - Money Management

When running a home, most people have to work to a budget. (*A specific amount they can afford to spend*).

When shopping, lots of money can be saved by finding the best buys for individual items.

Example :-

Lorne Dog Food comes in two sizes.

- The small one costs £2·65.
- The large one costs £3·64.

By calculating the cost of 100 grams of food for each size of tin, decide which is the better deal.

Cost of Small tin per 100 g :-

$$£2·65 ÷ 5 = £0·53.$$

Cost of Large tin per 100 g :-

$$£3·64 ÷ 7 = £0·52.$$

Better Deal is large tin.
A saving of 1p per 100 g.

Exercise 2

1. Zad Soap Powder is offered in two different sizes.
   - The Small box costs £14·40 for 600 grams.
   - The Large box costs £17·60 for 800 grams.

   Which one is the better deal ? Explain.

2.  Puss Puss Cat Treats come in two sizes of tin.
   - The small tin costs £2·45 for 350 grams.
   - The large tin costs £4·40 for 550 grams.

   Which is the better deal ? *Explain.*

   (*Hint :- find the cost per 50 grams or the cost per gram*).

3. A box of Ricarde Chocolates costs £4·18 for a 475 gram box or £5·20 for a 650 gram box.

   Which is the better deal ? *Explain.*

4. Two bottles of the same wine are priced £8·40 for the 700 ml bottle and £9·50 for the one litre bottle. Which is the better deal ? *Explain.*

5. GROUPAT offers special deals at the Grand Hotel in Tollus.

   Which of the two deals is better value for money ? *Explain.*

   Four Nights £300

   Five Nights £330

6. Joanne is comparing two holiday companies offers.

Which of the two should she choose ? *Explain*.

7.  Fence Paint can be bought in two tin sizes - 750 ml and 2·5 litres.

The larger tin costs £27·50. The smaller tin costs £9·75.

Which of the two tins offers the better value ?

8. Three cartons of rice are on offer.

  · The small 800 gram carton costs £1·60.
  · The 2 kilogram carton costs £3·60.
  · The large 12·5 kilogram trade carton costs £20.

Which of the boxes offers :-

a   the best value   b   the poorest value ?

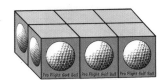

800 g   2 kg

9.  Golf balls are sold in boxes of 6, 16 and 24.

  · A box of six costs £10·20.
  · A box of sixteen costs £27·20.
  · A box of 24 costs £40·80.

Which would you choose ? *Explain*.

10. Noel paid £91·80 for 60 litres of diesel for his car at Texico.

Olive put 49 litres of diesel in her car at Jeet, costing £73·01.

Which petrol station offered the better deal ?

11. Mr Brown has a lawn 6 metres by 10 metres.
Mr White's lawn measures 8 metres by 12 metres.

  · Mr Brown paid £924 to have his lawn re-turfed.

  · Mr White paid £1344 to have a his lawn re-turfed.

Who got the better deal ?

12. At a local football match, Jake bought 6 pies and 4 bovrils which cost a total of £20·60.
Jake noticed that the price of a bovril was £1·55.

Alan was at another football match in the city.
He paid £12·30 for 3 pies (at £2·70 per pie) and 3 bovrils.

a   Who got the better deal on the pies ?

b   Who got the better deal on the bovrils ?

13. Investigate for yourself, or in a group, if buying goods in larger quantities always
provides a better value for money.

Best Deal – Services

Be able to find the best value when comparing different services

Most people in real life will "shop around" to find the best deal for service providers like plumbers, joiners etc.

Many of the service industry workers will charge a **call-out charge**, then a **rate per hour** and finally any **parts** or items that need purchased.

Example :-

* *PlumbMan* has a call-out charge of £40 and charge a rate of £32 per hour.

* *PlumbServices* have a £70 call-out charge and a £24 per hour rate.

Mrs Jackson needs a new sink and is told it will be a 5 hour job.

Which company should she choose ?

PlumbMan		*PlumbServices*	
labour £32 x 5 =	£160	labour £24 x 5 =	£120
callout	£40	callout	£70
total	**£200**	**total**	**£190**

She should use PlumbServices as it is **£10 cheaper**.

Exercise 3

1. a Mrs Jackson (above example) had miscalculated the time it would take to do her job. It actually only took 4 hours. Which company would have given the **better deal** ?

   b Mrs Jackson decided to have her whole bathroom renewed. PlumbMan gave her a quote for the job which would take 9 hours. PlumbServices quoted her for an 11 hour job.

   Which was the **cheaper** quote and by how much ?

2.  Jay's Joiners charge a rate of £36 per hour and have a £25 call-out fee. Kay's Carpenters have a £15 call-out charge and a rate of £28 per hour.

    Jay's have quoted Alex for a six hour job to floor his loft. Kay's have quoted seven hours to do the same job.

    a   Which provided the **lower quote** and by how much ?

    b   If the job took 9 hours, calculate each company's bill.

3. BG Media charge £80 call-out and £42·50 per hour. Vigin charges £47·50 per hour with a £70 call-out fee.

    Mrs Chalmers needs a new aerial installed (a two hour job).

    What would be the **cheaper** option ?

4. Two washing machine repair men have different charges.

   Bill — £75 for the 1st hour — £35 per hour thereafter
   Ben — Call-out charge £50 — £30 per hour

   Jackie employed Bill who took 3 hours to repair her washing machine.

   a How much was she charged in total ?

   b Would she have been **cheaper** if she had called Ben ?

5.  Greg called ElectroFix to rewire two of his rooms.

   ElectroFix had a call-out fee of £40 and charged £48 per hour for the 4 hour job.
   They also charged him for 14 metres of cable at £4·75 per metre.

   SparkServices would have charged him a call-out of £50, a rate of £59 per hour but the cable was included in the price.

   Would SparkServices have been **cheaper** ? (*Explain*).

6. Derek repairs washing machines.
   He charges according to the graph shown opposite.

   a After 0 hours what will he charge ? (*Hint – his call-out fee*).

   b What is his rate per hour ?

   c What would he charge in total for :-

      (i) 4 hours   (ii) 10 hours ?

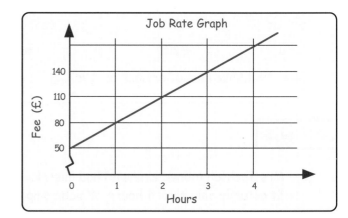

7. 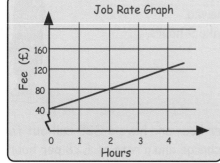 Alfie also repairs washing machines and he uses this graph to show his charges.

   a What is his call-out fee ?

   b What does he charge per hour ?

   c What would he charge for a job lasting :-

      (i) 5 hours   (ii) 11 hours ?

8. a Euan repairs cars from his mobile garage.
      He has a call-out charge of £30 and charges £40 per hour.

      Draw a graph, similar to that in question 6 and 7, to show Euan's fees.

   b On the same graph show Terry's charges of a call-out of £50 and a rate of £30 per hour.

   c Who charges **more** for a 2 hour job ?

   d How many hours are needed for Terry to be **cheaper** than Euan ?

   e How much would you save for an eight hour job by using Terry rather than Euan ?

9. Investigate for yourself, or in a group, different rates and charges for different services.

Best Deal - Rates or Contracts

Again, most people will wish to compare rates or contracts of telephone, internet and TV providers before taking out or renewing contracts with them, to make certain they are receiving the best value, and to save money.

Be able to find the best value when comparing different rates or contracts

Exercise 4

1. Mr Lee is looking for the best currency exchange rate to change his Yen into GBP (£'s). Xchange gives a rate of 13·45 Yen to the £. YenRate offers 13·6 Yen to the £.

   a   What rate should he take ? *Explain*.

   b   If Mr Lee has 4000 Yen, how much **more** would he get by choosing YenRate ?

2. Gerry has £2400 and is flying to Thailand. The exchange rate for 3 companies is :-

   > X-rate : £1 to 49·1 Baht   X - Money : £10 to 503 Baht   Xpound : £100 to 4898 Baht.

   How many **more** Baht will Gerry get from the **best** rather than the **poorest** deal ?

3. Two banks show the interest given on their deposit accounts.

   a   Which bank would you choose if you had £2000 to invest ?

   b   How much **more** per year would you get from your choice ?

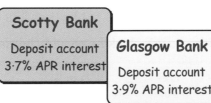

Scotty Bank

Deposit account 3·7% APR interest

Glasgow Bank

Deposit account 3·9% APR interest

4. Alice is looking at mobile phone tariffs.

Phone Company	Free mins	Free texts	Internet	Contract	Cost (monthly)
O3	100	1000	unlimited	12 months	£12
Oringe	100	1000	unlimited	24 months	£12

Explain why most people would choose O3.

5. Mrs Quinn is taking out a £8600 loan to buy a new car.

   Three companies offer different interest rates as shown :-

   a   Which company should she use ? (*Explain*).

   b   Calculate the **least** amount of **interest** she will have to pay for her loan ?

   c   How much will she save by taking the best rate rather than the poorest rate ?

CarLoan	- 11·5% interest
Loan Car	- 12% interest
Loans-R-us	- 15% interest

6. Shown is a table of Energy Suppliers' tariffs.

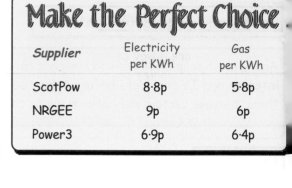

Make the Perfect Choice

Supplier	Electricity per KWh	Gas per KWh
ScotPow	8·8p	5·8p
NRGEE	9p	6p
Power3	6·9p	6·4p

a   Eddie uses ScotPow for gas and electricity. Last month he used 400 KWh (Kilowatt hour) of electricity and 1450 KWh of gas.

How much did he pay in total ?

b   Which company would have been cheapest supplying Eddie with both gas and electricity ?

c   How much would he have saved ?

d   Which is the best company to choose for his electricity and which is best for his gas ?

e   How much would he have saved if he had used these two companies ?

f   What would be the difference (if using two companies) between the cheapest and dearest options ?

7. Zara uses 4800 KWh of electricity and 18 350 KWh of gas during the year.

a   Decide which two companies she should choose and find her total bill.

b   Power3 offer 10% off the total bill if you take both electricity and gas.

Should Zara choose Power3 for both ? *Explain.*

8. a   Arthur is trying to decide which telephone provider to go with. He uses very few call minutes but he uses lots of texts.

Which provider do you think he should choose. (*Explain*).

Service Provider	Free Minutes	Free Texts	Internet Usage	Contract Period	Cost per Month
O3	100	100	unlimited	12 month	£9
Tangerine	200	1000	unlimited	24 month	£13
Small Talk	400	4000	unlimited	18 month	£20
Q-Mobile	100	5000	unlimited	12 month	£30
Dovafone	1000	5000	unlimited	12 month	£40

b   Amy has a budget of around £35 a month. She estimates she uses about 800 minutes of calls and approximately 4000 texts a month.

What would you advise her ?

c   Which would you choose from the table above ? Explain why you would choose this.

d   List some other things, not in the table, that you should consider when buying a contract.

9. Pick a service provider (e.g. gas, water, electricity, TV, phone, internet, etc.) Investigate different companies tariffs for your chosen subject. Which would you use ?

Write a report or project to show the findings of your investigation.

Credit & Debit Cards

Be able to understand the advantages and disadvantages of using a debit/credit card

Credit cards are a way of paying for something by borrowing money. Credit card companies charge a percentage of what you borrow each month if your account is in arrears - you owe them money.

Debit cards are bank related and money comes straight from your bank.

Exercise 5

Questions 1-4 could be tackled orally.

1. Discuss and list some of the advantages and disadvantages of using :-

    a a credit card   b   a debit card.

2. Leo is offered two credit cards as shown.

    a Find out what **APR** stands for.

    b Which card should he choose ? *Explain.*

    c What percentage interest would he pay **each month** for each of these cards ?

    d Leo owes £1200 at the end of the month.

       How much would he owe in interest from each card ?

Amix Card
Interest charge
36% APR

MNBA Card
Interest charge
30% APR

3.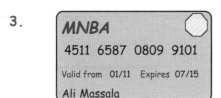

   Ali owes his *MNBA* credit card (see above) £2500. *Amix* ask him to transfer his MNBA debt to them, where he will pay no interest for three months.

   Write down or discuss whether he should accept. (*Give a reason for your answer*).

4. Rita owes her *Amix* card £3000 and her *MNBA* card £4500.

    a How much interest does she owe this month ?

    b How much interest would she pay over a year if she did not clear her debt ?

    c The real answer to b is quite a bit more than you think. Can you see why ?

5. Paul has been *very silly* over the last couple of years.

   He owes 4 credit cards the following amounts :-

       £5600, £8750, £4100, £6200.

   His credit card companies charge APR's of :-

       30%, 38%, 29% and 32% respectively.

   How much interest will Paul have to pay each month ?

6. Investigate different cards and APR's.

   Write a short report or presentation on your results.

1. Eazy Clean floor polish comes in 2 sizes. The 500 ml bottle costs £2·95 and the 2 litre plastic container costs £11·20.

    a   How much does it cost per 100 ml for the container ?

    b   How much does it cost per 100 ml for the bottle ?

    c   Which is better value ?

2. Which is the best buy here - the 6-pack, the 8-pack or the 9-pack of Cola ?

    £1·86   £2·32   £2·88

3. On my way back from Florida USA, I spent some time in Paris, France.

    When I got home, I had $192 and €168 left.

    If I changed them back to £'s, which would give the greater amount, and by how much ?

    Dollarate
    £1 = $1·60

    EuroChange
    £1 buys you €1·20

4. At one point, the exchange rate was €1·20 to the pound and 1 week later it was €1·25.

    a   When going on holiday from Scotland to Italy, which gives a better rate ? (*Explain*).

    b   Coming back from Italy I change my euros back to £'s. Which is the better ? (*Explain*).

5. Sheila travelled from Australia to Spain.

    She managed to obtain €1008 for her 1200 Australian dollars.

    What is the rate of exchange for Australian dollars to euros ?

6.

    I bought myself a new motorbike costing £7495.

    I took out a Hire Purchase contract agreement.

    I paid a deposit of £750 and £395 a month for 18 months.

    a   How much would I have saved if I had paid cash ?

    b   State 1 advantage and 1 disadvantage of using Hire Purchase to buy something.

7. I need to hire a cement mixer, to help build a garden wall.

    I estimate it will need to be hired for 6 hours.

    > *Tools 4 U* charge a basic hiring fee of £15 plus £8·50 per hour after that.
    >
    > *Hire-it-All* don't charge any basic fee but their rental charges are £10·25 per hour.

    a   Which company should I hire it from ? (*Explain*).

    b   It actually takes me 10 hours to build the wall.

        Would I have been better hiring it from the other company ? (*Explain*).

8.

    Jenny is having her lawn treated to help get rid of weeds.

    Greenfingers charge £3·80 per square metre as well as a charge of £8·50 for the fertiliser.

    Lawn Tidy charges £4·10 per square metre but the fertiliser only costs £4·50.

    Her lawn measures 25 square metres.

    Which company offers the **better** deal for her size of lawn ?

9. My electricity bill with *ScotPow* last year was £940.

    GlowGas charged me £1140 for my gas.

    I was offered a combined deal with *Electrogas* whereby my total bill for gas and electricity would have worked out at £165 per month.

    Should I have taken up *Electrogas'* offer ? (*Explain*).

10. Robyn was studying 3 different mobile phone providers' tariffs.

    | Tangerine | £17·50 per month | 200 min free - then 10p/min | 300 free texts then 10p/text |
    | Dovafone | £25 per month | 400 mins free - then 8p/min | 100 free texts then 10p/text |
    | P3 | £37·50 per month | 350 mins free - then 5p/min | free texting. |

    Last month, Robyn's statement said she used 410 minutes of calls and 240 texts.

    a   How much would it have cost Robyn each month with each of the 3 providers ?

    b   Which option should she choose ? (*Explain*).

    c   Robyn decided to take out a contract with "Tangerine".
        This month, she used 500 mins and 300 texts.

        Would she have been better off with Dovafone ?

    d   Write a short report stating what kind of user should go with which provider.

REVIEW 2

1. Round each of the following to 1 decimal place :-   a   9·749   b   0·666.

2. Round each of the following to 2 decimal places :-   a   12·5244   b   0·8973.

3. Round each of the following to 3 decimal places :-   a   1·0061   b   0·0096.

4. Round each of the following to 1 significant figure :-   a   5399   b   65 001.

5. Round each of the following to 2 significant figures :-   a   0·00396   b   5 465 320.

6. Round each of the following to 3 significant figures :-   a   125 099   b   0·03798.

7. How many significant figures have each of the following numbers been rounded to :-

    a   0·06007   b   0·0300   c   105 309 ?

8. Round each number to one significant figure and give an approximate answer to each :-

    a   217 x 51   b   3109 x 189   c   0·209 x 315

    d   8809 ÷ 32   e   784 200 ÷ 1884   f   0·3751 ÷ 1·84.

9. As part of a bird monitoring programme, the public reported seeing 45 475 sparrows in May.

    Round this to :-   a   2 significant figures   b   1 significant figure.

10. Rounded to 2 significant figures, the number of bees in a hive was 4700.

    What was the greatest number of bees there could have been in the hive ?

11. During the course of 32 flights, a businessman discovered
    he had flown a total of 58 765 miles.

    Approximately, how many miles did he travel on each flight ?

12. Calculate :-

    a   34 x 20   b   123 x 300   c   204 x 5000

    d   7600 ÷ 40   e   96 000 ÷ 8000   f   50 400 ÷ 700.

13. Carefully, work out the answers to the following :-

    a   15 - 6 x 2   b   20 - 12 ÷ (4 + 2)   c   8 + 10 ÷ 2.

14. Re-write the following and insert brackets to make each of the statements correct :-

    a   6 + 2 x 3 = 24   b   18 ÷ 3 + 6 = 2   c   2 + 3 x 5 - 3 = 10.

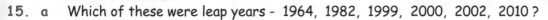

You may use a calculator in this section, but please show all working.

15. a   Which of these were leap years - 1964, 1982, 1999, 2000, 2002, 2010 ?

    b   I changed £3500 to euros before going to Germany .

        The rate was £1 = €1·23.

        How many euros did I receive ?

    c   I opened my piggy bank and discovered the following number of coins :-

        275 - 1p coins   123 - 2p coins   65 - 5p coins   84 - 10p coins

        72 - 20p coins   15 - £1 coins   6 - £2 coins, and some 50p coins.

        Altogether, I found that I had saved £75·26. How many 50p coins must I have had ?

16.

Henry measured his average walking stride.

It was 95 centimetres.

He went on a 5 kilometre charity walk.

How many steps would Henry have taken during the walk ?

17.   My new Mazda MX5 was priced £19 750 in the car showroom.

I paid it up monthly as follows :-

   •   an initial payment of £1975 (10%),

   •   followed by 36 monthly payments of £545.

How much less would it have cost me if I'd paid cash ?

18.

A large tin of soup weighs 750 grams.
Tins were packed into a cardboard box and weighed.

Altogether, the tins and the box weighed 36·5 kilograms.

The box weighs less than 1 tin of soup.

   a   Calculate how many tins were in the full box ?

   b   How heavy must the empty box have been ?

19.   This "Goody Bag" contains 20 items - a mixture of
Chewy Lollies (15 grams) and Sugar Mice (20 grams).

The total weight of the 20 items is 375 grams.

How many Lollies and how many Sugar Mice are in the bag ?

20.

1 lolly and 4 Chocy Bars cost 72p.
2 lollies and 2 Chocy Bars cost 54p.

How much will I pay for 1 lolly and 2 Chocy Bars ?

CHAPTER 3

Multiples and Lowest Common Multiple

Be able to list multiples of numbers and state their lowest common multiple

By now, you should know your **times** tables really well.

Example :- $9 \times 1 = 9$, $9 \times 2 = 18$, $9 \times 3 = 27$, $9 \times 4 = 36$, ...

The 9, 18, 27, 36, ... are sometimes referred to as "stations of 9".

More often, they are given their proper name :- "the **multiples of 9**".

Examples :-

> The first seven multiples of 9 are (0), 9, 18, 27, 36, 45, 54, ...
>
> The first five multiples of 4 are (0), 4, 8, 12, 16, ...

* Since "0" is always a multiple, (the trivial multiple), for the rest of this chapter we will ignore it.

Exercise 1

1. List (**not** including 0) :-

   a   the first **ten** multiples of 4   b   the first **eight** multiples of 3

   c   the first **nine** multiples of 5   d   the first **seven** multiples of 10.

2. a   Write down all the multiples of 3 between 8 and 25.

   b   Write down all the multiples of 6 between 29 and 61.

   c   Write down all the multiples of 8 between 23 and 73.

   d   Write down all the multiples of 9 between 53 and 100.

3. a   List the first ten multiples of 2.

   b   There is a special name for the "**multiples of 2**". What is it ?

   c   Subtract 1 from each of the numbers you have in part a and write them down.

      Is this a set of multiples ?

   d   What is the special name for this group of numbers ?

4. {14, 21, 28, 35, 42} could be described as "**the multiples of 7 from 14 to 42**".

   Describe the following sets of numbers in the same way :-

   a   {44, 46, 48, 50, 52, 54, 56}   b   {35, 40, 45, 50, 55, 60}

   c   {120, 130, 140, 150, 160}   d   {60, 66, 72, 78, 84, 90}

   e   {81, 90, 99, 108, 117}   f   {60, 80, 100, 120, 140}

   g   {15, 30, 45, 60, 75}   h   {600, 650, 700, 750, 800}

   i   {39, 52, 65, 78, 91}   j   {500, 750, 1000, 1250, 1500}.

5. a List the first twelve multiples of 3.

   b List the first twelve multiples of 4.

   c From a and b, write down the multiples which are "common" to both lists.
   (*The numbers that are multiples of both 3 and 4*).

   d What is the **lowest** number that is a multiple of both 3 and 4 ?

   This is called the "**lowest common multiple**" of 3 and 4 (*the l.c.m.*)

6. a List the first ten multiples of 4.

   b List the first ten multiples of 6.

   c List the common multiples of 4 and 6.

   d What is the l.c.m. of 4 and 6 ?

7. a List the first twelve multiples of 5.

   b List the first fifteen multiples of 3.

   c List the common multiples of 5 and 3.

   d What is the l.c.m. of 5 and 3 ?

8. Find the l.c.m. of each of the following pairs of numbers.
   (hint :- *go through the multiples of the larger of the two numbers until you reach
           a number into which the smaller number divides exactly*)

   a 2 and 5   b 6 and 3   c 4 and 9   d 3 and 4

   e 9 and 6   f 4 and 10   g 5 and 6   h 7 and 8

   i 10 and 6   j 9 and 8   k 9 and 12   l 4 and 11.

9. Find the l.c.m. of :-   a 2, 3 and 5   b 3, 4 and 8   c 2, 5 and 8

   d 2, 5 and 10   e 2, 3 and 7   f 3, 6 and 9   g 6, 8 and 20.

10. Howard's timetable for his golf lessons is :-

    > • Driver lessons every 5 days.
    >
    > • Putter lessons every 6 days.
    >
    > • Sand Bunker lessons every 8 days.

    He had a lesson on all three on the same day.

    How many days after that is he scheduled to have all three lessons on the same day again ?

11. A christmas tree's lights are set so that :-

    > • the blue lights flash every 9 seconds.
    >
    > • the green lights flash every 12 seconds.
    >
    > • the red lights flash every 15 seconds.

    When they are switched on, they all flash together.

    How long will it be until they flash together again ?

Be able to write factors of numbers and state their highest common factor

1, 2, 4 and 8 are all the whole numbers which divide exactly into 8.

These numbers are called the **factors** of 8.

Examples :-

| The factors of 6 are :- | 1, 2, 3, 6. |
| The factors of 12 are :- | 1, 2, 3, 4, 6, 12. |

* The factors of any number always includes the **number itself** and **1**.

Exercise 2

1. The number 10 has **four** factors. What are they ?

2. List all **six** factors of 28.

3. List the **six** factors of 18.

Factors usually occur in **pairs**. In the example below, 1 and 24 are a pair, as are 2 and 12. 3 and 8 and 4 and 6 are also pairs.

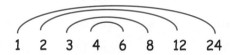

1   2   3   4   6   8   12   24

Using this **pairing** helps you not to miss out any of the factors.

4. Copy and complete the following, showing all the factors of 20.

1,   2,   4, ..., ..., ...

5. Use this method to find all the factors of :-

a	8	b	24	c	27	d	22
e	30	f	31	g	32	h	50
i	67	j	40	k	45	l	60.

6. Look at all your answers to Question 5.

Check that in each case, there is an **even** number of factors.

7. For each of the following, list all the factors and state how many factors each number has :-

| a | 9 | b | 49 | c | 36 | d | 4 |
| e | 25 | f | 64 | g | 16 | h | 100. |

8. a   Check that your answer to each question in Q7 has an **odd** number of factors.

    b   What is the special name for these numbers ?   {4, 9, 16, 25, 36, ...}

    c   Can you explain why there will always be an odd number of factors for this type of number ?

9. 36 apples are laid out in rows.
    One way is to have 4 rows of 9 apples.

    State a few other ways of laying out the 36 apples.   (2 rows of ...., etc)

10. a   List all the factors of 12.   {1, 2. .... }

    b   List all the factors of 18.   {1, 2. .... }

    c   Make a list of the common factors of 12 and 18. (those that appear in both lists).

    d   What is the largest of these numbers ?

    This number is referred to as the **highest common factor** (or h.c.f.) of 12 and 18.

11. a   List all the factors of 15.   b   List all the factors of 20.

    c   Make a list of the common factors.

    d   What is the h.c.f. of 15 and 20 ?

12. Find the highest common factor for each of the following :-

    a   6 and 9   b   12 and 20   c   20 and 30   d   24 and 28

    e   24 and 36   f   40 and 100   g   17 and 34   h   18 and 42.

13. Find the h.c.f. of :-

    a   7 and 23   b   31 and 41   c   11 and 17   d   53 and 67.

14. Find the h.c.f. of :-

    a   8, 12, 20   b   10, 20, 45   c   14, 35, 56   d   24, 32, 40.

15. A full revolution is divided into 360 parts. Each part is called "1 degree".

    The choice of 360 is no accident*.

    The reason is that 360 has many factors (**24** in fact) and this means a circle can be divided equally in lots of ways.

    Write down all 24 factors of 360.

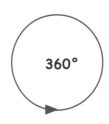

360°

16. There is only one number which is both a **multiple** and a **factor** of 1000. Which number ?

17. *   The Mayan calendar had a year of 360 days which meant, every day, the earth moved 1 degree in its orbit around the sun.
        This was possibly another reason why the circle was divided into 360 bits.

        Investigate other ancient and modern calendars.

Be able to list all the prime numbers up to 100 and possibly beyond

Examine how many **factors** these two groups of numbers have :-

6 has 4 factors   {1, 2, 3, 6}
8 has 4 factors   {1, 2, 4, 8}
12 has 6 factors   {1, 2, 3, 4, 6, 12}
20 has 6 factors   {1, 2, 4, 5, 10, 20}
32 has 7 factors   {1, 2, 4, 6, 8, 16, 32}

5 has 2 factors   {1, 5}
7 has 2 factors   {1, 7}
11 has 2 factors   {1, 11}
19 has 2 factors   {1, 19}
23 has 2 factors   {1, 23}

There is a special name for the numbers in the right hand box - the ones with only 2 factors.

They are called PRIME NUMBERS.

They are said to be the most important group of numbers in the study of arithmetic.

Every number can be divided by itself and 1.

Every prime number can only be divided by itself and 1.

A prime number is a number with exactly 2 factors.

Exercise 3

1. Write all the factors of 10. Why is 10 not a prime number ?

2. Write all the factors of 3. Why is 3 a prime number ?

3. How many factors has the number 14 ? Is 14 a prime number or not ?

4. Explain why the number 1 is not a prime number.

5. For each of the following numbers :-

    - list all of its factors, and state whether or not it is a prime number.

a	5	b	16	c	15	d	17
e	23	f	27	g	29	h	35
i	44	j	47	k	51	l	62.

6. A number which is not a prime, is called a **composite** number.

    State which of the following numbers are composite :-

    20, 37, 42, 33, 36, 37, 40, 41, 43, 49, 50.

7. Is 2 a prime number ? Give a reason for your answer.

8. a How long would it take you to write down all of the odd prime numbers ?

    b How long would it take you to write down all of the even prime numbers ? Try it.

9. a   Make a neat large copy of
        this number square showing
        all the numbers from 1 to 100.

1	2	3	4	5	6	7	8	9	10
11	12	13	14	15	16	17	18	19	20
21	22	23	24	25	26	27	28	29	30
31	32	33	34	35	36	37	38	39	40
41	42	43	44	45	46	47	48	49	50
51	52	53	54	55	56	57	58	59	60
61	62	63	64	65	66	67	68	69	70
71	72	73	74	75	76	77	78	79	80
81	82	83	84	85	86	87	88	89	90
91	92	93	94	95	96	97	98	99	100

    b   On your copy, score out the number 1.

        It is not a prime number.

    c   Don't score out 2 but score out every other
        multiple of 2 – (4, 6, 8, ... 100).

    d   Keep 3. Score out every other multiple of 3 – (6, 9, 12, ... 99).

    e   Keep 5. Score out every other multiple of 5 – (10, 15, 20, ... 95).

    f   Keep 7. Score out every other multiple of 7 – (14, 21, 28, ... 98).

    g   Now draw a circle round every remaining number in the square.

        You will find that these are all the prime numbers.

    h   Make a list of all the primes from 1 to 100. *Might be a good idea to learn them !*
        (*There are exactly 25 of them*).

10. a   Make up a grid similar to the one in Q9 for all the numbers from 101 to 200.

    b   Score out every multiple of 2, 3, 5 and 7 as in Q9.

    c   Now score out every multiple of 11.

    d   Lastly score out every multiple of 13.

    e   Circle all the remaining numbers – these are the primes from 101 to 200.

    f   Make a list of all the primes from 101 to 200. (*There are 21 of them*).

It is not difficult to check whether a large (*but not too large*) number is a prime or not.

You simply have to check if the number can be divided by all the primes 2, 3, 5, 7, 11, 13, etc, smaller than the number and if none of the primes (below it) divide into it, then the number must be prime.

The study of prime numbers has fascinated mathematicians for hundreds of years.

---

11. (As of 23rd August 2003, the largest known Prime was $2^{(13\,466\,917)} - 1$) with 4 053 917 digits.

     (This means (2 x 2 x 2 x 2 x ...... (13 466 917 times)) then take away 1).*

     Investigate what the largest prime number is at this time.

12. There are obvious reasons why some numbers are not prime.

     In each case below, say why they are not prime :–

     a   37495   b   1264572   c   89479480   d   3396303.

13. Find out about the Greek mathematician, Eratosthenes
     and how he was involved with prime numbers.

Prime Decomposition

Be able to express a number as a product of primes

Every number is either **prime** or **composite**, except for 0 which is neither.

If it is composite, like 18, it can be expressed as a "**product of primes**".

> This means that composite numbers can be factorised in such a way as to be written as a series of prime numbers multiplied together.

$$18 = 2 \times 9 = 2 \times 3 \times 3 \qquad \text{(3 prime numbers)}$$
$$60 = 2 \times 30 = 2 \times 2 \times 3 \times 5 \qquad \text{(4 prime numbers)}$$
$$64 = 2 \times 32 = 2 \times 2 \times 2 \times 2 \times 2 \times 2 \quad \text{(6 prime numbers)}$$

Here is an easy way of doing it for the number 40 :-

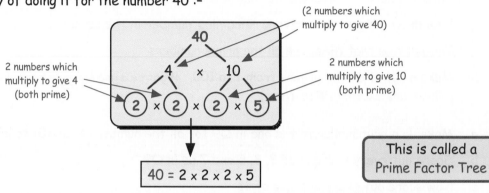

2 numbers which multiply to give 4 (both prime)

(2 numbers which multiply to give 40)

2 numbers which multiply to give 10 (both prime)

$$40 = 2 \times 2 \times 2 \times 5$$

This is called a **Prime Factor Tree**

Exercise 4

1. Copy this diagram and complete it to show the prime decomposition of the number 60.

    So $60 = 2 \times 2 \times ... \times ...$

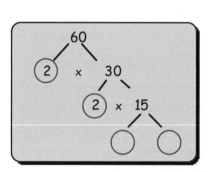

2. Copy and complete these prime factor trees :-

    a
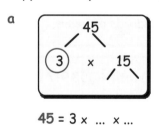

$45 = 3 \times ... \times ...$

    b

   36
   2   ×   18
            3

$36 = 2 \times 3 \times ... \times ...$

    c
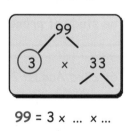

$99 = 3 \times ... \times ...$

3. Use a similar method to find the prime decomposition of the following numbers :-

    a   16   b   18   c   20   d   27

    e   30   f   54   g   45   h   48

    i   68   j   98   k   100   l   162.

4. a   Find the prime decomposition of 60 starting with (5 x 12), (4 x 15) and (30 x 2).

    b   Do you get a different final answer each time ? What does this tell you ?

1. Write down the :-

   a first ten non-zero multiples of :- (i) 4 and of (ii) 5.

   b lowest common multiple (l.c.m.) of 4 and 5.

2. Write down the lowest common multiple (l.c.m.) of :-

   a   6 and 9   b   15 and 25   c   4, 5 and 6.

3. Write down the :-

   a   factors of 10 and of 15

   b   highest common factor (h.c.f.) of 10 and 15.

4. Write down the highest common factor (h.c.f.) of :-

   a   18 and 24   b   20 and 70   c   27, 45 and 108.

5. a   Write down all the numbers, under 10, that have exactly two factors.

   b   Write down three numbers with exactly three factors.

6. a   What is the lowest common multiple of the numbers 2, 3, 4, 5, 6 and 7 ?

   b   What is the highest common factor of the numbers 95, 96, 97, 98 and 99 ?

7. How many factors does a prime number have ?

8. Write down all the prime numbers between :-

   a   20 and 30   b   50 and 60   c   90 and 110.

9. Write down TRUE or FALSE for each of the following statements :-

   a   There are no even prime numbers.

   b   If you multiply any two prime numbers, the answer you get is always a prime.

   c   Twenty one thousand four hundred and forty five is NOT a prime number.

10. Write down why each of these numbers are definitely not prime numbers :-

    a   483 792   b   sixteen million   c   99 999.

11. a   Write down the highest common factor (h.c.f.) of 17 and 23.

    b   Make a statement about the highest common factor of ANY two prime numbers.

12. Write each of the following numbers as the product of prime factors :-
    (For example, 18 = 2 x 3 x 3 and 50 = 2 x 5 x 5).

    a   15   b   54   c   75   d   256.

REVIEW 3

Percentages, Fractions & Decimals

1. Change each percentage to a decimal and then to a fraction in its simplest form :-

   a   50%   b   35%   c   10%   d   25%

   e   27%   f   12·5%.   g   64%   h   100%

   i $33\frac{1}{3}$ %   j   2%   k $66\frac{2}{3}$ %   l   150%.

2. Change each of the following into a percentage :-

   a   0·45   b   0·9   c   0·03   d   0·80

   e $\frac{7}{10}$ f $\frac{2}{5}$ g $\frac{13}{20}$ h $\frac{16}{25}$

   i   1·6   j   0·004   k $2\frac{1}{2}$ l   0·01.

3. Find :-

   a $\frac{3}{10}$ of £240   b $\frac{2}{5}$ of 80 euros   c   1% of £5600

   d   75% of 360 litres   e $12\frac{1}{2}$ % of $8000   f   0·3 of 250 km

   g $33\frac{1}{3}$ % of €150   h   0·7 of 3000 ml   i   81% of 2000 mm.

4. a   A jug, containing 800 ml of water, was placed on a window ledge.

   Two hours later, 20% of the water had evaporated.

   How much water was left in the jug ?

   b    450 fans went to watch Motherton play in their opening match.

   They played so badly that **two fifths** of them left at half-time.

   How many fans stayed on after half-time ?

   c   House prices in Ridgewater rose by 15% last year.

   A detached bungalow was valued at £210 000 before the rise.

   How much will it cost to buy the bungalow this year ?

   d    Wee Johnnie's mum measured his height at 140 cm in 2012.

   During 2012-2013, his height increased by 7%.

   How tall was Johnnie when measured in 2013 ?

This is a calculator section. ✓

5. Find :-

     a   35% of £260   b $\frac{5}{9}$ of 1467 euros   c   7% of £18 000

     d   0·85 of £28·60   e $37\frac{1}{2}$ % of £20 400   f $\frac{9}{11}$ of 6820 mg

     g $\frac{1}{2}$ % of £750   h   0·3 of $12\frac{1}{2}$ % of $\frac{3}{4}$ of $8000.

6.   a    The McDuff's were quoted a total price of £720 for their flights.

        They received an email saying flight prices had risen by 7·5%.

        What will the McDuff's have to pay now for their flights ?

    b   Shed and Holder's new shampoo bottle holds 16% more shampoo.

       I used to be able to get 75 washes from the old shampoo bottle.

       How many times can I wash my hair with the new one ?

7.   a    GameZone bought in 25 new Crazy Cult computer games for £450.

        The owner hopes to make at least a 45% profit by selling the games.

        What must he sell each game for to make the required profit ?

    b   The distance from the Earth to the Moon is 384 400 kilometres.

       A spacecraft had only travelled 62·5% of this journey when its rockets failed.

       How far **short** of the moon was the spacecraft at that time ?

8.   An Education Authority presented 850 pupils for a maths exam in 2012.

        22% of those presented failed to pass the exam.

        How many pupils did pass ?

9.   List these people in order, beginning with the one with the **largest** new annual salary.

      • Tania earns £350 per week and gets a weekly rise of £35.

      • Chas earns £19 500 per year and is given a 5·5% wage rise.

      • Donna is paid £1545 per month and her pay rises by a fifteenth.

10.    Janie bought a new computer and printer from QD World.

        She made an initial deposit of 15% of the cash price followed by 18 monthly payments of £36·50.

        How much **more** expensive was this than the cash price ?

CHAPTER 4

Revision – Sequences and Patterns

> **Remember :–** the rule for defining this sequence of numbers
>
> 6, 9, 12, 15, ... is *start at 6 and add 3 each time.*

Be able to recognise and continue a basic sequence of numbers

Exercise 1

1. Give a possible rule used in these sequences :- (*begin with* " *start at ... and then .....*").

   a   2, 5, 8, 11, 14, ...
   b   7, 13, 19, 25, ...
   c   25, 20, 15, 10, ...

   d   98, 81, 64, 47, ...
   e   3, 9, 27, 81, ...
   f   1, 6, 36, 216, ...

   g   200, 100, 50, 25, ...
   h   192, 48, 12, 3, ...
   i   1, 4, 16, 64, ...

   j $1\frac{1}{2}$, 2, $2\frac{1}{2}$, 3, ...
   k $5\frac{3}{4}$, $5\frac{1}{4}$, $4\frac{3}{4}$, $4\frac{1}{4}$, ...
   l   1, 2, 4, 8, ...

   m   200, 100, 0, –100, ...
   n   108, 36, 12, 4, ...
   o   2, 1, 2, 1, ...

2. Write down the next two numbers in each sequence from question 1.

3. Find two more numbers for each sequence :-

   a   7, 9, 11, 13, ...
   b   5, 9, 13, 17, ...
   c   24, 22, 20, ...

   d   70, 58, 46, 34, ...
   e   1, 3, 9, ...
   f   2, 4, 8, 16, ...

   g   96, 48, 24, ...
   h   1000, 100, 10, ...
   i   1, 6, 11, 16, ...

   j   2, 3, 5, 8, ...
   k   3, 4, 6, 9, ...
   l   2, 6, 12, 20, 30, ...

4. Shown is the pattern for **square numbers**.
   Write down the first 20 square numbers.

       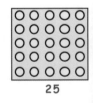

      1   4   9   16   25

5. a   Copy the first 4 patterns shown.
      This is the sequence of **triangular numbers**.

   b   How many dots did you have to add to
      the 3rd pattern to get to the 4th ?

   c   How many dots will you have to add
      to the 4th pattern to get to the 5th ?

      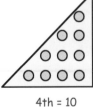

     1st = 1   2nd = 3   3rd = 6   4th = 10

   d   The 10th triangular number is 55. What is the :– (i) 11th   (ii) 12th   (iii) 13th ?

   e   Write down a relationship between the 68th and 69th triangular numbers.

   f   Write down the first 20 triangular numbers.

6. Shown is the first six rows of **Pascal's Triangle**.

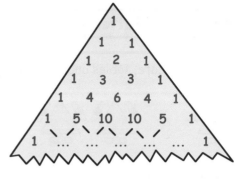

    a   **Copy** these first 6 rows of the triangle.

    b   Describe how to find the numbers in the next row.

    c   Write out the next 4 rows.

    d   Write down or discuss any patterns
        or sequences you can see.

7. a   Copy and extend this pattern for four more rows.

        Discuss the patterns used, then **write down** the :-

$$2^2 - 1^2 = 4 - 1 = 3 = 2 + 1$$
$$3^2 - 2^2 = 9 - 4 = 5 = 3 + 2$$
$$4^2 - 3^2 = 16 - 9 = 7 = 4 + 3$$

    b   10th row   c   25th row

    d   100th row   e nth row.

8. a   Add the first two **triangular numbers.**   (1 + 3).

    b   Add the 2nd and 3rd triangular numbers.   (3 + ...).

    c   Add the 3rd and 4th triangular numbers.

    d   Add the 4th and 5th triangular numbers.

    e   What do you notice about your answers ?

9. a   Which two *consecutive* triangular numbers add to give 36 ?

    b   **Write down** the sum of :-

        (i)   the (9th + 10th) triangular numbers.   (ii)   the (99th + 100th) triangular numbers.

10. a   Write down each of these values :-

        $\frac{1}{2}(1 \times 2)$, $\frac{1}{2}(2 \times 3)$, $\frac{1}{2}(3 \times 4)$, $\frac{1}{2}(4 \times 5)$.

    b   What do you notice about this sequence of numbers ?

    c   Copy and complete :-   "the nth pattern is $\frac{1}{2}(n \times ....)$".

    d   Can you find the 1000th triangular number ?

Work in a small groups to investigate each of these problems :-

11. Twenty people arrive at a meeting.
    Each person shakes hands with every other person.

    How many handshakes are there altogether ?

12. How many squares are on a chessboard ?

    (The answer is **not** 64).

13. How many diagonals would there be in a decagon ?

    (A decagon is a ..... sided shape).

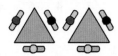 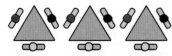

Simple Linear Patterns

Be able to identify and use a formula for a basic linear pattern

In the school cafe, tables and chairs are arranged as shown.

1 table
3 pupils

2 tables
6 pupils

3 tables
9 pupils

Putting these values into a table helps you see a pattern :-

No. of tables (T)	1	2	3	4	5	6
No. of Pupils (P)	3	6	9	12	?	?

+3   +3   +3

Can you see that for every new triangular table => the number of pupils rises by 3 ?
=> we can write this in words as :-

number of Pupils = 3 x number of Tables

=> or in symbol form :- $P = 3 \times T$

Exercise 2

1.   Each filing cabinet has 4 drawers.

   a   Copy and complete the table :-

No. of Cabinets (C)	1	2	3	4	5	6
No. of Drawers (D)	4	8	?	?	?	?

   rises by :   ⟶   4   4   ?   ?   ?

   b   Write down a formula showing the relationship between C and D. (ie $D = ... \times C$).

1 cabinet
4 drawers

2 cabinets
8 drawers

   c   Use your formula to find how many :-

      (i)   drawers you need if you have 20 cabinets.

      (ii)   cabinets you require if you have 60 drawers.

2.   Here is a pattern of teddies, (T), and buttons, (B).

   a   Construct a table similar to question 1.

   b   Copy and complete the formula :- $B = ... T$

   c   How many buttons do you need for 9 teddies ?

   d   How many teddies do you need for 72 buttons ?

1 Teddy
6 buttons

2 Teddies
12 buttons

3. For each of the tables below :- (i) complete each one (ii) construct a formula.

a No. of cakes and price

C	1	2	3	4	5	6
P	40	80	120	...	...	...

$P = \text{.......} \times C$

b No. of Starfish and no. of arms

S	1	2	3	4	5	6
A	5	10	15	...	...	...

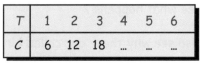

$A = \text{.......} \times S$

c No. of days and no. of hours

D	1	2	3	4	5	6
H	24	48	72	...	...	...

$H = \text{.......} \times D$

d No. of chairs to tables

T	1	2	3	4	5	6
C	6	12	18	...	...	...

$C = \text{.......} \times T$

e No. of dogs and no. of legs

D	1	2	3	4	5	6
L	4	8	12	...	...	...

f No. rooms to no. of chairs

R	1	2	3	4	5	6
C	31	62	93	...	...	...

g No. of calculators and no. of buttons

C	1	2	3	4	5	6
B	12	24	36	...	...	...

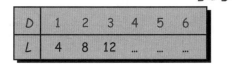

h No. of erasers and no. of boxes

B	1	2	3	4	5	6
E	66	132	198	...	...	...

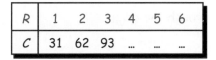

4. For both of these tables :-

(i) complete each table (ii) construct a formula

(iii) find y given $x = 20$ (iv) find x given $y = 60$.

a

x	0	1	2	3	4	5
y	0	2	4	6	...	...

$y = \text{.......}$

b

x	0	1	2	3	4	5
y	0	3	6	9	...	...

$y = \text{.......}$

5. A machine turns at a constant speed and completes ten revolutions every three seconds.

No. of seconds (S)	3	6	9	12	?	?
No. of Revs (R)	10	20	30	...	...	...

a Complete the table to show the number of revs (R) and the time taken.

b Make a formula to show the relationship between the revs and the time.

c Use your formula to find :-

(i) how many revs for 60 seconds (ii) how many seconds for 110 revs.

Look again at the table from question 4a.

We can show this pattern as

$y = 2x$.

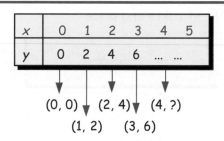

x	0	1	2	3	4	5
y	0	2	4	6	...	...

Consider each pair of numbers as a **coordinate pair** and plot them on a Cartesian graph.

(0, 0) (2, 4) (4, ?)

(1, 2) (3, 6)

Can you see what happens ?

Can you also see why these are called **Linear** Patterns ?

It can be seen that $y = 2x$ can be represented graphically as a **straight line** ?

Also notice that this line of coordinates passes through the origin.

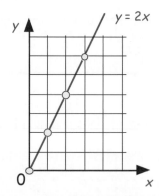

6. For each of the tables below :-

(i)   complete each table

(ii)   construct a formula

(iii)   take each pair of numbers as coordinates

(iv)   plot the points on a coordinate graph

(v)   draw a line through the points and label the line with your formula.

a

x	0	1	2	3	4	5
y	0	3	6	9	...	...

b

x	0	1	2	3	4	5
y	0	4	8	12	...	...

c

x	0	1	2	3	4	5
y	0	5	10	15	...	...

d

x	0	1	2	3	4	5
y	0	6	12	18	...	...

e

x	0	1	2	3	4	5
y	0	7	14	21	...	...

f

x	0	2	4	6	8	10
y	0	1	2	3	...	...

7. Repeat question 6 instructions for these tables :-   (*Grids should show all 4 quadrants*).

a

x	-2	-1	0	1	2	3
y	...	-1	0	1	2	...

b

x	-2	-1	0	1	2	3
y	...	-2	0	2	4	...

c

x	-2	-1	0	1	2	3
y	...	-3	0	3	6	...

d

x	-2	-1	0	1	2	3
y	...	2	0	-2	-4	...

Be able to identify and use more difficult linear patterns

Remember our simple pattern of tables and chairs for the school cafe.

Consider what would happen if we rearranged the tables in this way :-

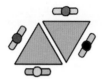 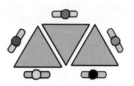

| 1 table | 2 tables | 3 tables |
| 3 pupils | 4 pupils | 5 pupils |

For each additional table the number of pupils rises by 1.

No. of tables (T)	1	2	3	4	5	6
No. of Pupils (P)	3	4	5	6	?	?

+1 +1 +1

But $P = 1 \times T$ doesn't work this time !

Check $1 \times 1 \neq 3$ $1 \times 2 \neq 4$ $1 \times 3 \neq 5$ $1 \times 4 \neq 6$ .....

but $1 \times 1 + 2 = 3$ $1 \times 2 + 2 = 4$ $1 \times 3 + 2 = 5$ $1 \times 4 + 2 = 6$ .....

A correction number is required to make this pattern work. In this example the number is + 2

=> $P = 1 \times T + 2$ *Example* :- With 10 tables you need $P = 1 \times 10 + 2 = $ 12 pupils

1.   Here is another pattern with tables and chairs.

 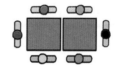 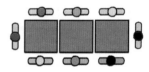

| | 1 table | 2 tables | 3 tables |
| 4 customers | 6 customers | 8 customers |

a   Copy and complete the table below to show this relationship :-

No. of tables (T)	1	2	3	4	5	6
No. of customers (C)	4	6	8	...	...	...

2   2   2

b   Copy and complete the formula for this pattern :- $C = ... \times T + ...$

c   Use this formula to find the number of customers around 20 tables.

d   Use this formula to find the number of tables needed for 30 customers.

2. This pattern is made up of equilateral triangles:-

 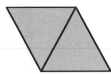 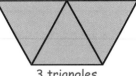 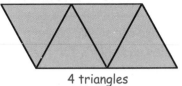

| 1 triangle | 2 triangles | 3 triangles | 4 triangles |
| 3 lines | 5 lines | 7 lines | .... lines |

a Copy the following table and complete it :-

No. of triangles (T)	1	2	3	4	5	6
No. of lines (L)	3	5	7	...	?	?

? ? ?

b Write down the formula using **symbols** :- L = ? x T + ?.

c Use your formula to decide how many lines are needed to place 30 triangles in a row as in the pattern above.

d If 31 lines are used to make one of the above patterns, how many triangles must there have been ?

3. Look at the pattern of fence posts and support panels :-

 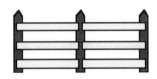 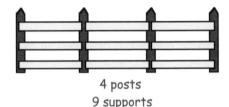

| 2 posts | 3 posts | 4 posts |
| 3 supports | 6 supports | 9 supports |

a Copy the following table and complete it :-

No. of posts (P)	2	3	4	5	6	7
No. of supports (S)	3	6	9	?	?	?

3 ? ?

This time the correction number has to be subtracted

b Write down the formula using symbols :- S = ? x P - ?.

c Use your formula to decide how many support panels are needed with 20 posts.

d Use your formula to find how many posts are needed if you have 87 supports.

4. These "house shapes" are made up of squares and triangles.

 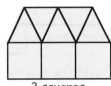 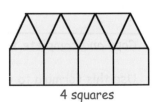

| 2 squares | 3 squares | 4 squares |
| 3 triangles | 5 triangles | 7 triangles |

4. **a** Copy the following table and complete it :-

No. of squares (S)	2	3	4	5	6	7
No. of triangles (T)	3	5	7	?	?	?

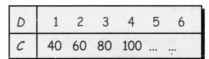
?   ?   ?

b Write down the formula using **symbols** :- $T = ? \times S - ?$.

c Use your formula to decide how many triangles are needed with 25 squares.

d Use your formula to find how many squares you would have for 131 triangles.

5. This table shows the cost of hiring a car, where D is the number of days and C is the cost in £'s.

D	1	2	3	4	5	6
C	40	60	80	100	...	...

a Write down the cost of hiring for 5 days and 6 days.

b Write down a formula showing this relationship.

c Find the cost of hiring a car for a fortnight.

d I paid £320 for my car hire. For how long did I have the car ?

6. For each of the tables below :-

(i) complete each table   **(ii)** construct a formula.

a

x	0	1	2	3	4	5
y	2	3	4	5	...	...

b

x	0	1	2	3	4	5
y	1	3	5	7	...	...

c

x	0	1	2	3	4	5
y	3	5	7	9	...	...

d

x	0	1	2	3	4	5
y	5	6	7	8	...	...

e

x	0	1	2	3	4	5
y	2	5	8	11	...	...

f

x	0	1	2	3	4	5
y	-1	2	5	8	...	...

g

x	-2	-1	0	1	2	3
y	...	-5	-3	-1	1	...

h

x	-2	-1	0	1	2	3
y	...	-6	-2	2	...	...

i

x	-2	-1	0	1	2	3
y	...	-3	-2	-1	0	...

j

x	-4	-2	0	2	4	6
y	...	2	0	-2	-4	...

k

x	0	1	2	3	4	5
y	2·5	3	3·5	4	...	...

l

x	0	1	2	3	4	5
y	1·3	2·5	3·7	4·9	...	...

We can show this pattern as

$$y = 2x + 1.$$

Again, consider each pair of numbers as a coordinate and plot them on a Cartesian graph - (*this time showing all 4 quadrants*).

Can you see that $y = 2x + 1$ can be represented graphically as a straight line ?

Notice where the line cuts the y-axis.

Notice how steep the graph is.

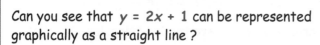

x	-2	-1	0	1	2	3
y	-3	-1	1	3	5	7

(-2, -3)   (0, 1)   (2, 5)

(-1, -1)   (1, 3)

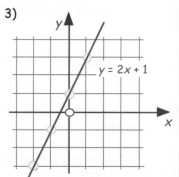

y = 2x + 1

7. For each of the tables below :-

    (i)   complete each table   (ii)   construct a formula

    (iii) take each pair of numbers as a coordinate   (iv)   plot the points on a coordinate graph.

    (v)   draw a line through the points and label the line with your formula.

a

x	-2	-1	0	1	2	3
y	-2	0	2	4	…	….

b

x	-2	-1	0	1	2	3
y	1	2	3	…	…	…

c

x	-2	-1	0	1	2	3
y	0	2	4	…	…	…

d

x	-2	-1	0	1	2	3
y	…	…	-1	1	3	…

e

x	-2	-1	0	1	2	3
y	-4	-3	-2	…	…	…

f

x	-2	-1	0	1	2	3
y	-9	-5	-1	3	…	…

g

x	-2	-1	0	1	2	3
y	-3	0	3	…	…	…

h

x	-2	-1	0	1	2	3
y	…	0	4	8	…	…

i

x	-2	-1	0	1	2	3
y	-10	-8	-6	…	…	…

j

x	-2	-1	0	1	2	3
y	…	0	5	10	…	…

k

x	-4	-2	0	2	4	6
y	…	0	2	4	…	….

l

x	-2	-1	0	1	2	3
y	3	3	3	3	…	…

8. Discuss each of the above graphs - look at each formula and where the line crosses the y-axis and the steepness of each graph.

Revisit - Review - Revise

1. Write down the next two numbers in these sequences :-

   a   80, 73, 66, 59, 52, ...   b   225, 196, 169, 144, 121, ...

   c   2, 6, 12, 20, 30, ...   d   1, 2, 5, 10, 20, ...

2. If you add any 2 consecutive triangular numbers together, you get a square number.

   For example :-   1 + 3 = 4, 3 + 6 = 9, 6 + 10 = 16, etc...

   Which 2 consecutive triangular numbers add to give the square number 100 ?

3. The table below shows the weight in grams of a bag with lollies in it.

No. of lollies (L)	1	2	3	4	5	6
Weight in grams (W)	50	85	120			

   a   How heavy will the bag be with 4 lollies ?

   b   Write down the formula for the weight of the bag with L lollies.

   $$W = \ ....$$

   c   How heavy will a full bag be if it contains 20 lollies ?

4. A necklace is made up using a mixture of purple Amethyst stones and Diamonds.

   2 Amethysts   3 Amethysts   4 Amethysts   5 Amethysts
   3 diamonds   6 diamonds   9 diamonds   12 diamonds

   a   Derive a formula for the number of Diamonds D in terms of the number of Amethysts A.

   $$D = \ ....$$

   b   How many Amethysts would you need if you had 87 diamonds ?

5. Shown below are four tables showing the connection between pairs of values.

   Write down a formula connecting the value of the 2nd letter in the table to the 1st letter.

   a
h	1	2	3	4
P	1	4	9	16

   $P = \ ......$

   b
m	1	2	3	4
T	12	19	26	33

   $T = \ ......$

   c
x	1	2	3	4
D	1	7	13	19

   $D = \ ......$

   d
c	1	2	3	4
N	2	5	10	17

   $N = \ ......$

REVIEW 4

1. Find :-

 a   6 – 11   b   -5 + 9   c   18 + (-12)   d   7 - (-3)

 e   -7 - (-2)   f   -51 - (-53)   g   -2 + (-6) - (-8)   h   -3 - (-11).

2. Find :-

 a   -2 + 3 - (-4) + (-5)   b   20 - (-13) + (-18) - 15   c   75 + (-81) - (-96).

3. Find :-

 a   5 x (-4)   b   (-2) x (-7)   c   24 ÷ (-3)   d   (-28) ÷ (-7)

 e   3 x (-4) x 2   f   (-4) x (-3) x (-2)   g   (-59) x (-13) x 0   h   (-40) ÷ (-5) x (-3).

4. Find :-

 a   8 - (-2) x (-3)   b   -4 x (-5) + (-6) ÷ (-2)   c   (-2) x (-2) - (-2) x (-2).

5. At the end of May, Lena's bank balance was -£545.

 a   What does a "balance of -£545" really mean ?

 Her monthly salary of £1725 was paid in on 1st June and
 she paid for her T in the Park tickets, costing £360.

 b   What was Lena's new balance ?

6.    When Scott left England to travel to the Antarctic,
 the temperature was $18°C$.

 When he arrived, it had dropped to $-29°C$.

 By how much had the temperature changed ?

7. Simplify the following expressions :-

 a $p + p + p$ b $m \times m$ c $4d \times 5e$ d $9a + 5b - a - 7b$

 e $p^2 \times 4p$ f $5t \times 3t^2$ g $20x^2 \div 5x$ h $4s \times 9s \div 6s$.

8. Work out the value of these expressions when $a = 9$, $b = 4$ and $c = -3$:-

 a $2a + b$ b $a^2 - b^2$ c $(b - c)^2$ d $2b^2$

 e $\sqrt{a}$ f $\dfrac{a - c}{b}$ g $\dfrac{ab^2}{c^2}$ h $\sqrt{b^2 + 2a - 5c}$.

9. Multiply out the brackets :-

 a $4(3x + 2)$ b $7(6a - 3b)$ c $g(g + 5)$ d $3y(4y - 7z)$

 e $-6(d - 5)$ f $-a(a - 4b)$ g $-2w(5 - w)$ h $-q^2(q - 4r)$.

10. Expand the brackets and then simplify :-

　　a　$3(x + 4) - 9$　　　　　　b　$5 + 4(m - 2)$　　　　　　c　$3(h + 4) + 2(h - 5)$

　　d　$9(g - 2) + 7(g + 3)$　　　e　$3(2b - 1) - 2(b - 3)$　　　f　$5d - (3 - d)$.

11. This shape is made up of a rectangle with a
　　right angled triangle on top, (*a trapezium*).

　　Write down an expression for the
　　total area of the shape, in terms of x.

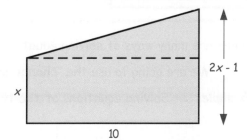

12. Determine the value of the capital letter :-

　　a　$G = 2p - q$　　　　　　Find G, when $p = 13 \cdot 5$ and $q = 21$.

　　b　$S = \dfrac{w - x}{y}$　　　　　Find S, when $w = 15$, $x = -6$ and $y = 7$.

　　c　$D = \sqrt{b^2 - c^2}$　　　　Find D, when $b = 13$ and $c = 12$.

You may use a
calculator for the
rest of this exercise

13. To change a number of miles into kilometres :-

　　| Multiply the miles by eight, then divide your answer by five. |

　　Change 140 miles into kilometres.

14. To change from degrees Fahrenheit (°F) to degrees Celsius (°C) :-

　　| Subtract 32 then divide your answer by 1·8. |

　　Change 68°F to °C.

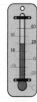

15. To find the monthly repayments of a 1 year bank loan :-

　　| Add on 8% of the loan to the loan, then divide this total by 12. |

　　a　Calculate the interest (the 8%) on an annual loan of £3600.

　　b　Calculate the monthly repayments.

16.　　　　　　　　　　　　a　Write down the formula for the circumference of a circle.

　　15 cm　　　　　　　　　b　Calculate the circumference of this circle.

17.　a　Construct a formula for finding P, the **perimeter**
　　　of the **symmetrical** shape shown opposite.

　　b　Find P, when $a = 12$ cm, $b = 8$ cm and $c = 15$ cm.

　　c　Find c, when $P = 42$ mm, $a = 6 \cdot 5$ mm and $b = 4 \cdot 3$ mm.

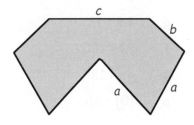

CHAPTER 5

Solving Equations

Be able to solve simple equations

There are many ways of solving equations.

We are going to use the "change side - change sign" method.

* your teacher may show you an alternative method

Examples :- Solving equations of the type $x + a = b$.

move the +4 to the other side => change it to –4

$$x + 4 = 9$$
$$\Rightarrow \ x = 9 - 4$$
$$\Rightarrow \ x = 5$$

$$x - 7 = 17$$
$$\Rightarrow \ x = 17 + 6$$
$$\Rightarrow \ x = 23$$

$$x - 9 = -2$$
$$\Rightarrow \ x = -2 + 9$$
$$\Rightarrow \ x = 7$$

Exercise 1

1. Copy each equation and solve to find the value of x, as shown above :-

   a $\quad x + 2 = 5$ b $\quad x + 9 = 19$ c $\quad x + 6 = 11$

   d $\quad x + 12 = 12$ e $\quad x - 3 = 4$ f $\quad x - 8 = 1$

   g $\quad x - 17 = 0$ h $\quad x - 20 = 30$ i $\quad x + 9 = 6$

   j $\quad x - 7 = 0$ k $\quad x + 13 = 0$ l $\quad x - 16 = 29$

   m $\quad 9 + x = 1$ n $\quad 4 + x = 4$ o $\quad 22 + x = 0$

   p $\quad 11 + x = 4$ q $\quad 8 + x = 8$ r $\quad 19 + x = -19.$

Examples :- Solving equations of the type $ax = b$.

move the x4 to the other side => change it to ÷4

$$4x = 28$$
$$\Rightarrow x = 28 \div 4$$
$$\Rightarrow x = 7$$

$$3p = -27$$
$$\Rightarrow p = -27 \div 9$$
$$\Rightarrow p = -3$$

$$5k = 18$$
$$\Rightarrow k = 18 \div 5$$
$$\Rightarrow x = \frac{18}{5} = 3\frac{3}{5}$$

2. Copy each equation and solve to find the value of the letter :-

   a $\quad 2x = 16$ b $\quad 5p = 45$ c $\quad 3k = 24$

   d $\quad 3h = 21$ e $\quad 4g = 36$ f $\quad 7n = 7$

   g $\quad 8m = 12$ h $\quad 13c = 0$ i $\quad 4d = 1$

   j $\quad 3y = 120$ k $\quad 10s = 300$ l $\quad 6w = 21$

   m $\quad 4a = 13$ n $\quad 5b = 29$ o $\quad 7e = 23$

   p $\quad 10j = 65$ q $\quad 8q = 2$ r $\quad 3r = 29.$

Examples :- Solving equations of the type $ax + b = d$.

Move the –4 to the other side and change to +4

move the $x2$ to the other side and change to ÷ 2

$$2x - 4 = 10$$
$$\Rightarrow \quad 2x = 10 + 4$$
$$\Rightarrow \quad 2x = 14$$
$$\Rightarrow \quad x = 7 \text{ (divide)}$$

$$8x + 9 = 57$$
$$\Rightarrow \quad 8x = 57 - 9$$
$$\Rightarrow \quad 8x = 48$$
$$\Rightarrow \quad x = 6$$

$$6x - 3 = 24$$
$$\Rightarrow \quad 6x = 24 + 3$$
$$\Rightarrow \quad 6x = 27$$
$$\Rightarrow \quad x = 27 \div 6 = 4\tfrac{1}{2}$$

3.   Find the value of x in the following equations (*Set down each step of working carefully*).

a $2x + 4 = 10$ b $6x + 3 = 21$ c $5x + 2 = 47$

d $3x + 5 = 29$ e $4x - 3 = 37$ f $7x - 2 = 5$

g $10x - 6 = 44$ h $8x - 8 = 0$ i $9x - 7 = 38$

j $7x - 3 = 39$ k $3x + 12 = 15$ l $8x + 1 = 65$

m $6x - 6 = 36$ n $10x + 23 = 123$ o $5x + 4 = 44$

p $2x - 1 = 14$ q $12x + 12 = 0$ r $3x - 8 = 0$

s $4x + 10 = 8$ t $6x + 3 = 30$ u $4x - 7 = 6$.

Harder Equations

This diagram shows a set of balanced scales.

- 5 blocks and a 4 kg weight on the left

- 2 blocks and a 10 kg weight on the right.

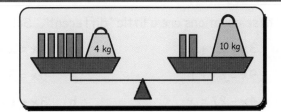

If each block weighs x kg, then the equivalent equation for this is :-

$$5x + 4 = 2x + 10$$ –   to be solved.

To simplify the situation, remove
2 blocks ($2x$) from both sides.

This leaves a much simpler equation, $3x + 4 = 10$,
which you already know how to solve.

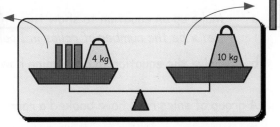

* your teacher
may show you an
alternative
method

remove $2x$ from both sides

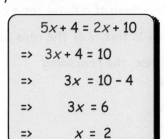

$$5x + 4 = 2x + 10$$
$$\Rightarrow \quad 3x + 4 = 10$$
$$\Rightarrow \quad 3x = 10 - 4$$
$$\Rightarrow \quad 3x = 6$$
$$\Rightarrow \quad x = 2$$

$\Rightarrow$ 1 block must weigh 2 kg.

(*Check this works on the diagram above*).

Examples :- Solving equations of the type $ax + b = cx + d$.

Take $3x$ from both sides.

Move the $+2$ to the other side and change to -2

move the $x4$ to the other side and change to $÷4$

$$7x + 2 = 3x + 22$$
(take "$3x$" from each side)
$$\Rightarrow \quad 4x + 2 = 22$$
$$\Rightarrow \quad 4x = 22 - 2$$
$$\Rightarrow \quad 4x = 20$$
$$\Rightarrow \quad x = 5$$

$$9x - 1 = 4x + 14$$
(take "$4x$" from each side)
$$\Rightarrow \quad 5x - 1 = 14$$
$$\Rightarrow \quad 5x = 14 + 1$$
$$\Rightarrow \quad 5x = 15$$
$$\Rightarrow \quad x = 3$$

$$8x + 7 = 2x + 28$$
(take "$2x$" from each side)
$$\Rightarrow \quad 6x + 7 = 28$$
$$\Rightarrow \quad 6x = 28 - 7$$
$$\Rightarrow \quad 6x = 21$$
$$\Rightarrow \quad x = 21 ÷ 6 = 3\tfrac{1}{2}$$

Exercise 2

1. Copy and complete

   a $\quad 6x + 1 = 4x + 19$
   $$\Rightarrow \quad 2x + 1 = ...$$
   $$\Rightarrow \quad 2x = ...$$
   $$\Rightarrow \quad x = ...$$

   b $\quad 8x - 5 = x + 16$
   $$\Rightarrow \quad 7x - ... = ...$$
   $$\Rightarrow \quad 7x = ...$$
   $$\Rightarrow \quad x = ...$$

2. Solve these equations by removing the correct number of x's from each side first :-

   a $\quad 4x + 3 = 2x + 9$
   b $\quad 3x + 2 = x + 18$
   c $\quad 6x + 6 = 5x + 18$

   d $\quad 10x - 9 = 7x + 12$
   e $\quad 6x - 1 = 2x + 23$
   f $\quad 6x - 4 = x + 41$

   g $\quad 13x - 3 = 9x + 29$
   h $\quad 10x - 7 = 8x + 8$
   i $\quad 4x + 8 = x + 26$

   j $\quad 6x + 9 = 2x + 11$
   k $\quad 3x + 22 = 9x - 2$
   l $\quad x + 1 = 9x + 9$.

3. These equations are a little "different". Solve them in the same way as shown above :-

   a $\quad 3x = 2x + 3$
   b $\quad 5x = x + 16$
   c $\quad 6x = 3x + 36$

   d $\quad 9x = 8x + 1$
   e $\quad 5x = 3x + 17$
   f $\quad 7x - 9 = 5x$

   g $\quad 4x - 27 = x$
   h $\quad 3x + 13 = x$
   i $\quad 8x = 11x - 39$.

4. Joe bought 3 packets of rollos. Harry bought 1 packet, but he already had 20 loose rollos.

   They discovered that they then had exactly the same number of rollos.

   a Make up an equation to show this information.
   (*let x be the number of rollos in 1 packet*)

   b Solve the equation to determine how many rollos there are in a packet.

5. A group of sales reps have booked a room on the top floor of a hotel for a conference.

   They use the hotel elevator (full) 4 times and as well as this, 9 of the reps use the stairway.

   After the conference, the elevator is filled only **twice**, the remaining 25 reps using the stairway to go down to reception.

   a Make up an equation to show this information.
   (*let x be the number of reps in 1 full elevator*)

   b Solve the equation to determine how many reps were at the conference.

Solving Equations with Brackets

Examples :- Solving equations with brackets.

* your teacher may show you an alternative method

Multiply out the brackets

$$3(2x + 1) = x + 18$$
$$\Rightarrow \quad 6x + 3 = x + 18$$

Take "x" from both sides

$$\Rightarrow \quad 5x + 3 = 18$$

Move the +3 to the other side

$$\Rightarrow \quad 5x = 18 - 3$$

$$\Rightarrow \quad 5x = 15$$

Divide by 5

$$\Rightarrow \quad x = 3$$

$$4(3x + 5) - 2(4x - 1) = 2x + 20$$
$$\Rightarrow \quad 12x + 20 - 8x + 2 = 2x + 20$$
$$\Rightarrow \quad 4x + 22 = 2x + 20$$
$$\Rightarrow \quad 2x + 22 = 20$$
$$\Rightarrow \quad 2x = 20 - 22$$
$$\Rightarrow \quad 2x = -2$$
$$\Rightarrow \quad x = -1$$

Note :- the + 2 (not – 2)

Exercise 3

1. Solve these equations by multiplying out the brackets first :-

   a $2(x + 2) = 10$ b $3(x + 7) = 24$ c $5(x - 4) = 25$

   d $4(x + 3) = 44$ e $6(x + 3) = 60$ f $2(x + 5) = 12$

   g $10(x - 2) = 30$ h $8(x + 3) = 56$ i $4(x - 1) = 24$

   j $7(x - 1) = 0$ k $4(x - 1) = 2$ l $3(x + 4) = 6.$

2. Solve these equations :-

   a $2(4x + 1) = 10$ b $3(2x - 3) = 15$ c $4(5x - 2) = 12$

   d $2(4x + 5) = 26$ e $3(2x - 11) = 9$ f $2(5x - 5) = 0$

   g $3(2x - 2) = 4x + 12$ h $2(4x + 2) = 3x + 29$ i $2(1 + 3x) = 4x + 7$

   j $7(2x - 1) = 13x$ k $10(2x - 6) = 14x + 54$ l $10(x + 4) = 2x.$

3. Solve :-

   a $3(x + 2) - x - 6 = 10$ b $2(x + 2) + 3x - 8 = 16$

   c $5(x + 3) - 2x = 24$ d $5(x - 2) + 2x + 6 = 38$

   e $2x + 8 + 3(x - 2) = 12$ f $4x + 2(x - 4) = 10$

   g $2(x + 5) + 3(x - 3) = 21$ h $4(3x + 2) + 5(1 - 2x) = 25$

   i $4(2x + 1) + 2(x - 3) = 6x + 40$ j $2(3x - 5) + 4(x + 8) = 3x + 29$

   k $4(x + 8) - 2(x + 6) = 18$ l $8(x - 1) - 3(x - 2) = 18$

   m $3(3x + 1) - 2(x - 5) = x + 31$ n $13(x + 1) - 2(3x + 6) = 2x - 49.$

Solving Equations with Fractions

Fractions are a real nuisance in equations.

=> Fortunately, we can do away with fractions in equations quite easily.

> **Rule :-** Always **eliminate the fractions** at the beginning by **multiplying every term** by the l.c.m. of all the fractional denominators.

Examples :-

Multiply both sides by 2 to eliminate the one fraction $\frac{1}{2}$

$$\frac{1}{2}x + 4 = 9$$

$$2 \times \frac{1}{2}x + 2 \times 4 = 2 \times 9$$

$$=> \quad x + 8 = 18$$

$$=> \quad x = 18 - 8$$

$$=> \quad x = 10$$

The l.c.m. of 3 and 4 is 12.

Multiply both sides by 12 to eliminate both fractions $\frac{2}{3}$ and $\frac{3}{4}$

$$\frac{2}{3}x + \frac{3}{4} = 1$$

$$12 \times \frac{2}{3}x + 12 \times \frac{3}{4} = 12 \times 1$$

$$=> \quad 8x + 9 = 12$$

$$=> \quad 8x = 3$$

$$=> \quad x = 3 \div 8 = \frac{3}{8}$$

Exercise 4

1. Copy and complete the following two equations :-

   a
   $$\frac{1}{2}x + 3 = 7$$
   $$2 \times \frac{1}{2}x + 2 \times 3 = 2 \times 7$$
   $$=> \quad x + \ldots = \ldots$$
   $$=> \quad x = \ldots$$

   b
   $$\frac{3}{4}x - 5 = \frac{3}{5}x - 2$$
   $$20 \times \frac{3}{4}x - 20 \times 5 = 20 \times \frac{3}{5}x - 20 \times 2$$
   $$=> \quad 15x - \ldots = \ldots x - \ldots$$
   $$=> \quad 3x - \ldots = -40 + \ldots$$
   $$=> \quad \ldots x = \ldots$$
   $$=> \quad x = \ldots$$

2. Solve each of these equations, by first of all multiplying every term by the l.c.m. of all the fractional denominators. This should eliminate all the fractions.

   a $\frac{1}{2}x - 3 = 1$

   b $\frac{1}{4}x + 5 = 6$

   c $\frac{1}{8}x - 3 = 0$

   d $\frac{2}{3}x - 4 = 4$

   e $4 + \frac{4}{5}x = 16$

   f $\frac{5}{8}x + 4 = 14$

   g $\frac{3}{4}x + \frac{1}{2} = 5$

   h $\frac{1}{2}x + \frac{3}{5} = 1$

   i $\frac{2}{5}x + \frac{1}{3} = 1$

   j $\frac{1}{2}x - 1 = \frac{1}{4}$

   k $\frac{2}{3}x - 4 = \frac{1}{3}$

   l $\frac{3}{4}x - 1 = \frac{2}{3}$

   m $\frac{1}{2}x + 2 = \frac{1}{3}x + 4$

   n $\frac{3}{4}x - 1 = \frac{3}{5}x + 2$

   o $2 + \frac{3}{4}x = \frac{1}{3}x + 3$

   p $\frac{1}{2}x - \frac{1}{3} = \frac{3}{4}$

   q $\frac{1}{4}x + \frac{1}{2} = \frac{3}{5}$

   r $\frac{1}{3}x - \frac{1}{2} = \frac{1}{4}x + \frac{2}{5}$.

Solving Inequalities

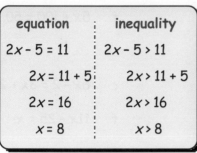
Be able to solve inequalities

$2x + 5 = 11$ and $3(x - 4) = 2x + 3$ are two examples of **equations**.

Inequalities are similar except the $=$ sign is replaced with one of :-
$<$, $>$, $\leq$ or $\geq$ each time.

Solving an inequality is almost identical to solving the corresponding equation.

equation	inequality
$2x - 5 = 11$	$2x - 5 > 11$
$2x = 11 + 5$	$2x > 11 + 5$
$2x = 16$	$2x > 16$
$x = 8$	$x > 8$

The solution this time is
"x can be any number
greater than 8"
(not $x = 8$)

equation	inequality
$4(2x - 1) = x + 17$	$4(2x - 1) \leq x + 17$
$8x - 4 = x + 17$	$8x - 4 \leq x + 17$
$7x - 4 = 17$	$7x - 4 \leq 17$
$7x = 21$	$7x \leq 21$
$x = 3$	$x \leq 3$

The solution this time is
"x can be any number smaller
than or equal to 3"
(note $x = 3$ is permitted)

Reminder :-   "$<$" - means "less than".
"$>$" - means "greater than".
"$\leq$" - means "less than <u>or</u> equal to".
"$\geq$" - means "greater than <u>or</u> equal to".

Exercise 5

1. Solve these inequalities, leaving your answers in the form $x > 2$, etc. :-

   a $x + 2 > 6$ b $x + 4 < 12$ c $x - 9 \leq 8$

   d $x + 7 \geq 12$ e $x - 6 \leq 6$ f $x - 14 \geq 0$.

2. Solve each inequality, leaving your answers in the form $x \leq 4$, etc. :-

   a $5x < 15$ b $4x > 32$ c $3x < 18$

   d $8x \geq 32$ e $9x \leq 54$ f $280 < 10x$.

3. Solving the following inequalities :-

   a $4x + 1 < 25$ b $2x + 3 > 11$ c $6x - 1 < 17$

   d $2x + 5 \geq 21$ e $10x - 2 \leq 48$ f $8x - 3 > 53$

   g $8x - 20 < 0$ h $20x - 20 \geq 20$ i $15 \geq 2x + 8$

   j $\frac{1}{2}x - 1 < 13$ k $\frac{1}{4}x + 6 \geq 11$ l $\frac{1}{5}x - 1 > 1$

   m $2(x + 3) < 20$ n $4(x - 3) \geq 36$ o $3(4x + 1) \leq 27$

   p $2(5x + 4) \leq -2$ q $\frac{1}{2}(2x - 8) > 0$ r $\frac{1}{9}(x - 3) < 2$

   s $7(x + 2) < 4x + 23$ t $5(2x + 2) > 6x + 20$ u $5x + 17 \leq 3(2x - 4)$.

1. Find the value of x in these equations :-

    a $x + 9 = 15$ b $5 - x = -1$ c $4x = 18$

    d $3x + 16 = 0$ e $7x - 2 = 54$ f $5x + 100 = 50.$

2. Solve each of the following equations :-

    a $7x - 1 = 6x + 8$ b $10x + 5 = 8x + 17$ c $6x - 2 = 3x + 22$

    d $9x + 3 = 5x + 31$ e $12x = 7x - 45$ f $11x - 25 = x.$

3. Solve these equations :-

    a $3(x + 2) = 24$ b $2(3x - 5) = 14$ c $4(1 + 3x) = 52$

    d $6(x - 5) - x = 0$ e $5(x + 1) - 3(x - 2) = 17$ f $4(3x - 1) = 9x + 23.$

4. Solve each of the following **inequalities**, leaving your answer in the form $x < 3$, $x \geq 5$ etc.

    a $x - 3 > 10$ b $5x \geq 45$ c $6x - 7 < 35$

    d $3(x + 4) \leq 33$ e $4(2x - 3) < 28$ f $7x - 2 \geq 4x + 19.$

5. Solve these equations and inequalities :-

    a $\frac{1}{2}x = 7$ b $\frac{1}{4}x + 3 = 8$ c $\frac{1}{3}x - 2 > 3$

    d $\frac{1}{2}(3x + 5) = 13$ e $\frac{1}{5}(x - 11) \leq 0$ f $\frac{1}{3}(4x - 5) = x.$

6. I'm thinking of a number (x). I multiply it by 4, then add on 30 to it.
   I then half this and take away 11. I end up with an answer of 20.

    a   Construct an equation to show this information.

    b   Solve the equation to determine the number I was thinking of to begin with.

7. Tommy is a joiner and he bought 6 boxes of
   screws, though he already had 40 loose ones.

   Alf, his apprentice, had 4 boxes of screws
   as well as 190 loose screws.

   They found they each had the same number of screws.

    a   Construct an equation to show this information.
        (*Let x represent the number of screws in a box*).

    b   Solve the equation to find how many screws there are in a full box.

REVIEW 5

 ✓  **Angles**

1. What is the :- a complement of 70° b supplement of 60° ?

2. Copy and complete each diagram below, filling in all missing angles :-

a
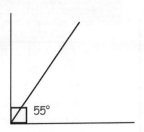
55°

b
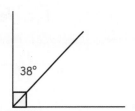
38°

c
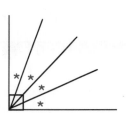

d

145°

e
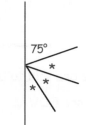
75°

f
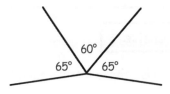
150°

g
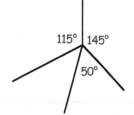
115° 145°
50°

h
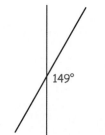
40°
120°

i
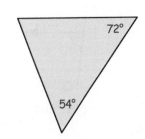
60°
65° 65°

j
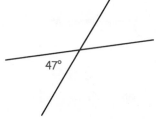
47°

k
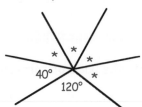
149°

l
72°
54°

m

n
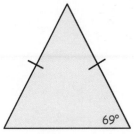
69°

o
36°

p
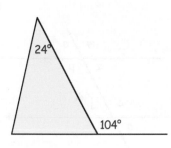
24°
104°

q
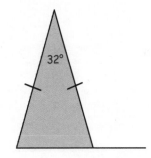
32°

r
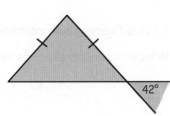
42°

CHAPTER 6

Corresponding Angles

Be able to find unknown angles using corresponding angles

Many mathematical figures have parallel lines in them.

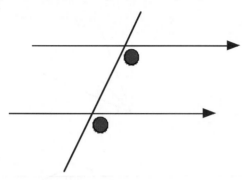

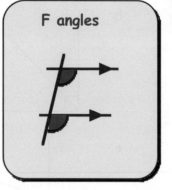

F angles

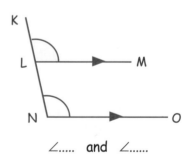

A line which cuts across 2 or more parallel lines is called a transversal.

The two angles shown in the above figure are said to be in "corresponding positions".

Note :-   Corresponding angles are EQUAL.

Exercise 1

1. Use three letters each time to name the pairs of corresponding angles :-

    a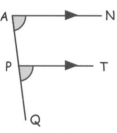

    ∠NAP and ∠.....

    b

    ∠..... and ∠.....

    c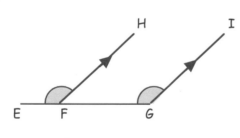

    ∠..... and ∠.....

    d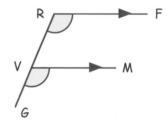

    ∠..... and ∠......

2. In this figure, **j** corresponds to **a**.

    Which angle corresponds to :-

    a **w**   b **f**   c **z** ?

    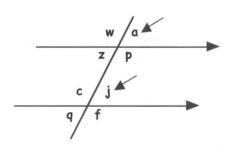

3. **COPY** the diagrams shown and mark the angles which **CORRESPOND** to the ones already marked.

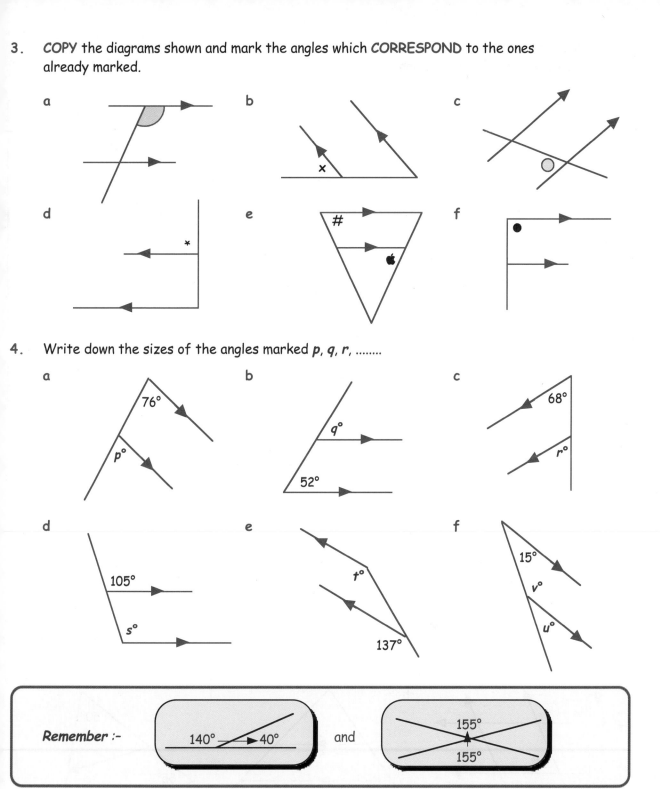

a

b ×

c

d *

e # 🍎

f ●

4. Write down the sizes of the angles marked *p*, *q*, *r*, ...

a 76° *p*°

b *q*° 52°

c 68° *r*°

d 105° *s*°

e *t*° 137°

f 15° *v*° *u*°

Remember :- 140° ⟶ 40° and 155° / 155°

5. Use the above facts, along with corresponding (*F*) angles, to help **COPY** the diagrams below and enter all the missing angles :-

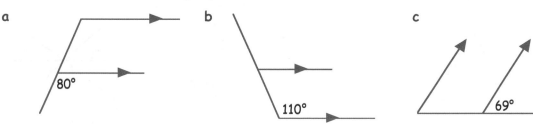

a 80°

b 110°

c 69°

6. Copy the figure shown opposite and fill in the sizes of all the missing angles.

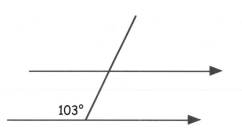

103°

7.

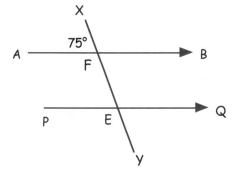

In this figure, ∠XFA = 75°.

a   Write down the size of ∠FEP.

b   Make a neat sketch of the figure and calculate the sizes of all the other angles.

8. Sketch each of the following and fill in all the missing angles :-

a

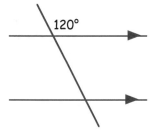

120°

b

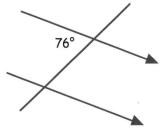

76°

c

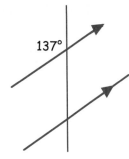

137°

d

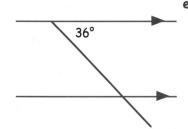

36°

e

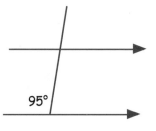

95°

f

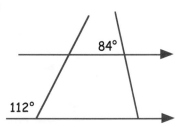

84°

112°

g

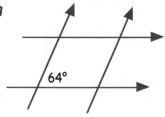

64°

h

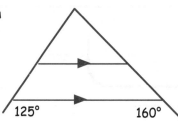

125°   160°

i

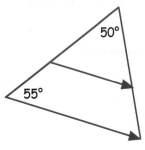

50°

55°

j

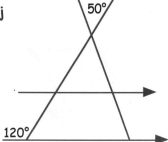

50°

120°

k

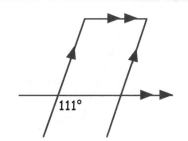

111°

l

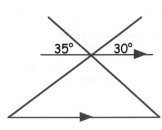

35°   30°

Be able to find
unknown angles
using alternate
angles

If a pair of parallel lines have a line
joining them, a Z- shape is formed :-

Z angles

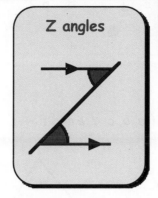

The two angles shown in the above figure are said to be in "alternate positions".

Note :-   Alternate angles are EQUAL.

Exercise 2

1.   Make a neat sketch of each of these figures and mark the angle which is
      alternate to the one already marked :-

a
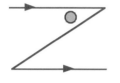

b
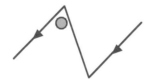

c

d
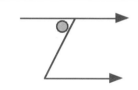

e
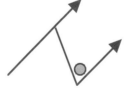

f
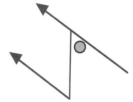

2.   Use three letters each time to name the pairs of alternate angles :-

a
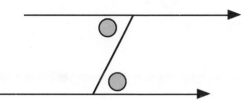

b
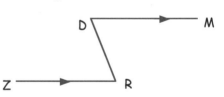

c
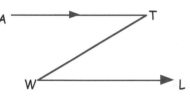

d
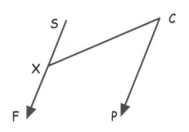

3. In this figure, which angle is **alternate** to :-

   a z   b c   c j   d p ?

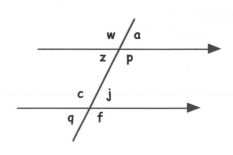

4. Write down the values of *a*, *b*, *c*, *d*, *e* and *f* :-

a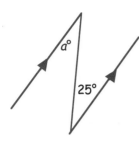

b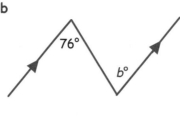

c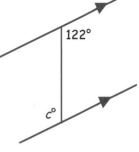

d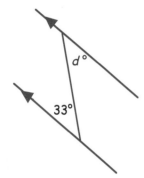

e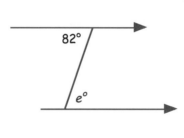

f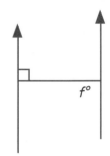

5. Copy the figure shown opposite.

   Fill in the sizes of all the missing angles.

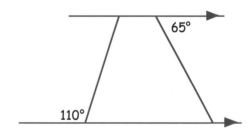

6. 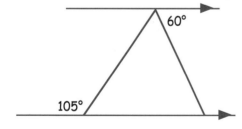 Make a neat copy of this figure and fill in all the missing angles.

7. Make a neat copy of this figure and fill in all the missing angles.

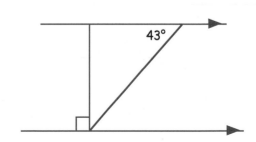

Remember :-

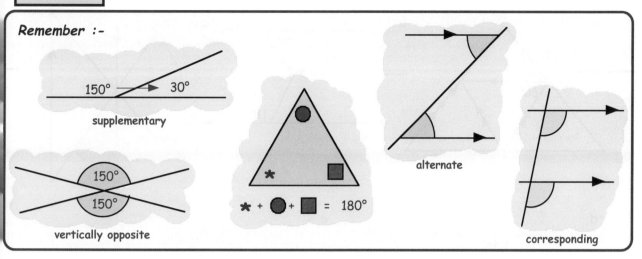

150° → 30°

supplementary

150° / 150°

vertically opposite

★ + ● + ■ = 180°

alternate

corresponding

1. Using the above facts, **sketch** the following diagrams **NEATLY** and mark in all the missing angles :-

a

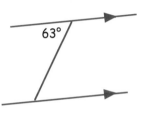

63°

b

100°

c

58° 70°

d

84°

e

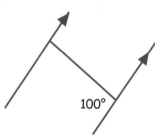

120°

110°

f

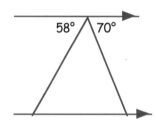

42°

g

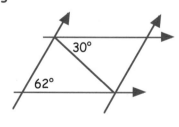

30°

62°

h

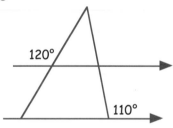

61°

i

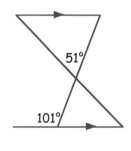

51°

101°

j

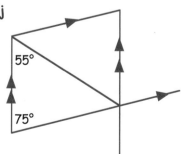

55°

75°

k

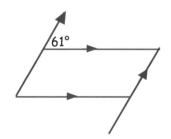

46°

l

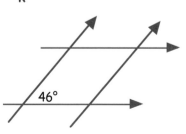

144°

2. These are harder :-

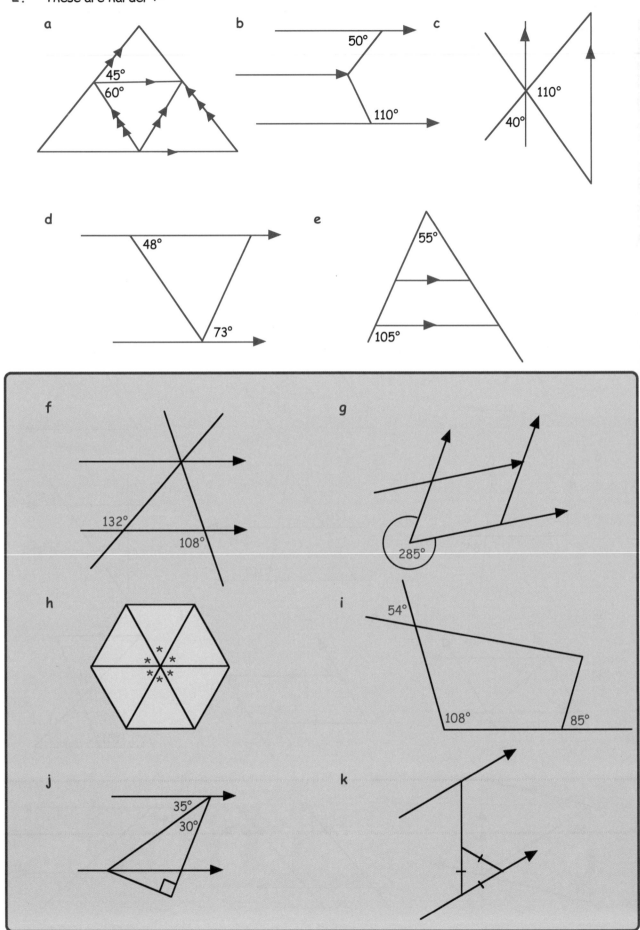

a

45°
60°

b

50°

110°

c

110°

40°

d

48°

73°

e

55°

105°

f

132°

108°

g

285°

h

* *
* *
* *

i

54°

108°   85°

j

35°
30°

k

1. a   What is the size of the angle which is complimentary to 34° ?

    b   Write down the supplement of 85°.

2. Make a neat sketch of each diagram and find the size of the angles marked with a letter.

a
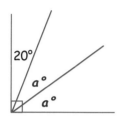

b
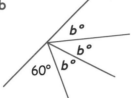

c
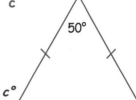

d
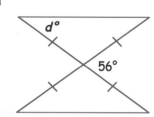

e
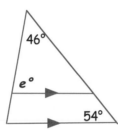

f
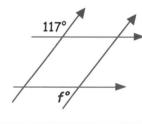

g
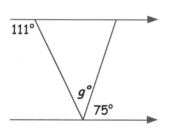

h
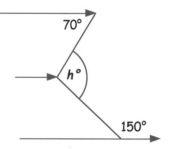

3. Make a copy of these two diagrams and enter the sizes of all their angles.

a

b

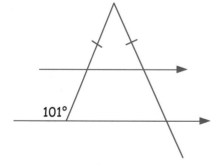
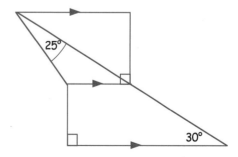

REVIEW 6

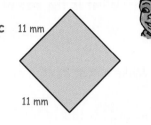

1. For each of these shapes, name the shape, state what formula should be used to find its area and then calculate its area.

a
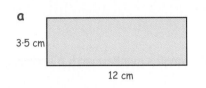

3·5 cm
12 cm

b
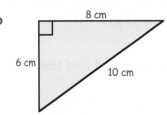

8 cm
6 cm
10 cm

c
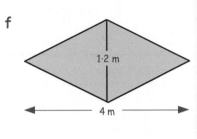

11 mm
11 mm

d
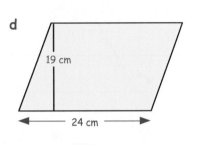

19 cm
24 cm

e
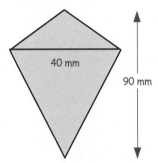

40 mm
90 mm

f
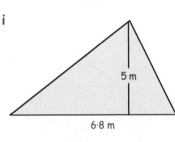

1·2 m
4 m

g
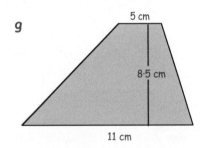

5 cm
8·5 cm
11 cm

h
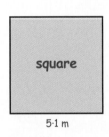

3·2 cm
6 cm

i
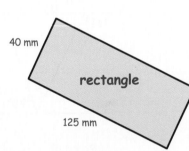

5 m
6·8 m

2. Calculate the perimeter of :-

a
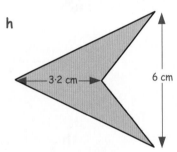

square
5·1 m

b

rectangle
40 mm
125 mm

3. Calculate the area of these composite shapes, showing each step of your working :-

a
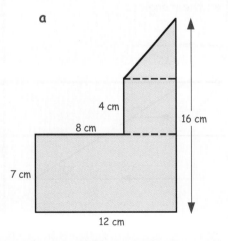

4 cm
8 cm
16 cm
7 cm
12 cm

b
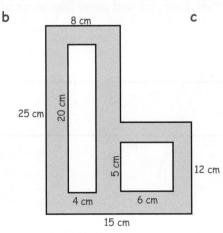

8 cm
25 cm
20 cm
5 cm
4 cm
6 cm
12 cm
15 cm

c
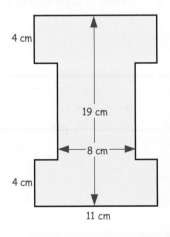

4 cm
19 cm
8 cm
4 cm
11 cm

4. Calculate the **volume** of this gift-box.

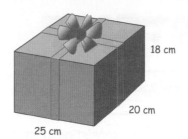

18 cm
20 cm
25 cm

5.

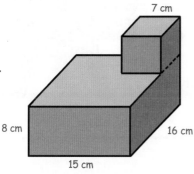

7 cm
8 cm
16 cm
15 cm

Calculate the **total volume** of this shape consisting of a cube on top of a cuboid.

6. Change to litres :-   a   3500 ml   b   270 ml   c   20 ml.

7. Change to ml :-   a $6\frac{3}{4}$ litres   b   2·005 litres   c $\frac{3}{5}$ litre.

8.

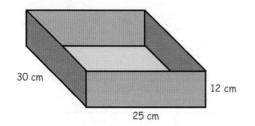

30 cm
12 cm
25 cm

This tray is used by a hotel to catch the water at the bottom of a fridge as it is being defrosted.

a   Calculate the **volume** of the tray in cm^3.

b   How many litres of water will it hold when full ?

9. It took 6 litres of water to create this ice cuboid.

Calculate the **depth** (*d*) of the ice cuboid.

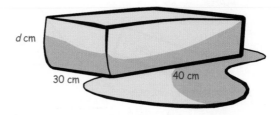

d cm
30 cm
40 cm

10.

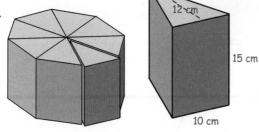

12 cm
15 cm
10 cm

This is an **octagonal prism** with one of its 8 identical sections shown.

Calculate the **volume** of the triangular prism and hence find the volume of the octagonal prism.

11. Calculate the **volume** of this shape, which consists of a triangular prism on top of a cuboid, which has a hole through its middle.

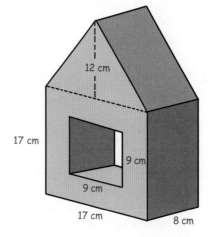

12 cm
17 cm
9 cm
9 cm
17 cm
8 cm

CHAPTER 7

Recognising Polygons

Be able to recognise and know names of polygons

A polygon is a flat shape consisting of straight lines that are joined to form a closed chain or a circuit.

In book 1a, you were asked to go online and look up the name of polygons with up to 12 sides. Now you will be asked to learn these names.

Exercise 1

1. Here are 15 polygons and 15 names. See if you can match each shape with its correct name.

    Have a good guess at any you don't know - but when you find out the correct name - learn it !

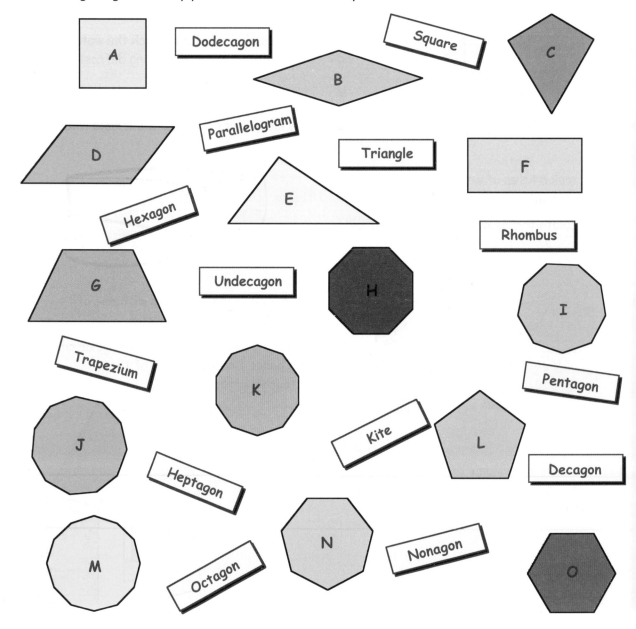

2. How many :-

    a   sides has a rectangle   b   diagonals has a square

    c   vertices has a triangle   d   sides has a pentagon

    e   diagonals has a hexagon   f   vertices has an octagon

    g   sides has a nonagon   h   diagonals has a heptagon

    i   vertices has a dodecagon   j   vertices has a nonagon

    k   diagonals has a decagon   l   vertices has a parallelogram

    m   sides has a kite   n   diagonals has a rhombus

    o   vertices has a trapezium   p   sides has a heptagon ?

3. There is a building in the USA called "The Pentagon".

    Why is the building so called, where exactly is it and what is it used for ?

Drawing Triangles   You will require :- a RULER, a PROTRACTOR and a PAIR of COMPASSES.

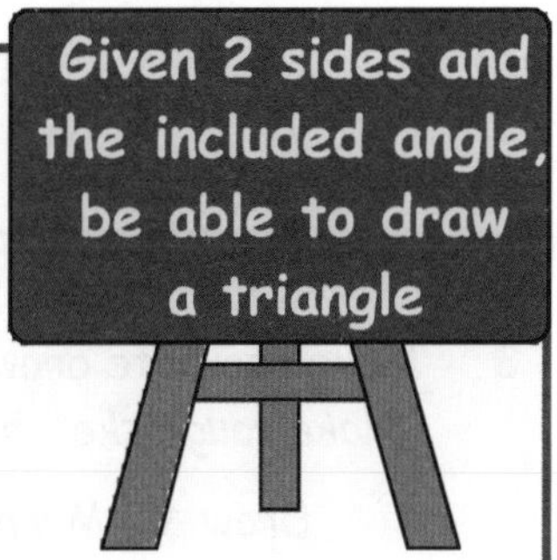

> **Given 2 sides and the included angle, be able to draw a triangle**

Given 3 relevant pieces of information about a triangle, you should be able to draw it accurately.

Two Sides and the Included Angle
(*the angle between the 2 sides*)

Here is a sketch of △ABC.

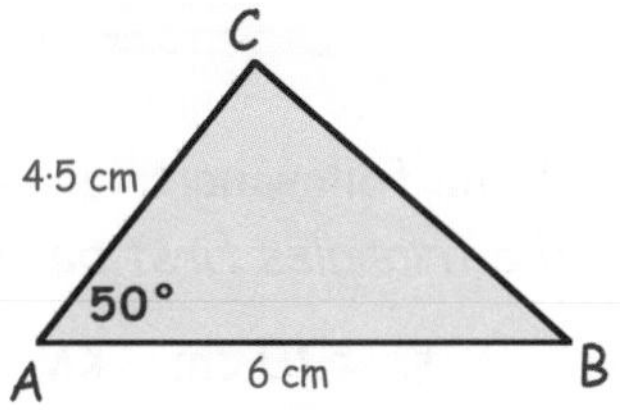

To draw it accurately :-

Step 1 :-   Draw a line AB = 6 cm.

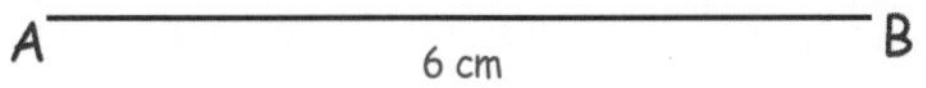

Step 2 :-   Place your protractor at A and mark an angle of 50°.

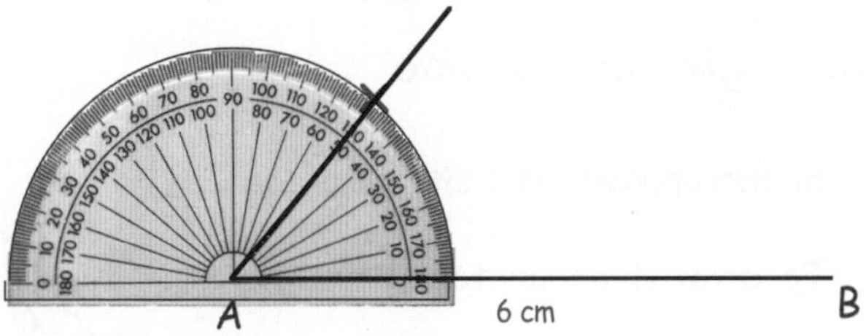

Step 3 :-   Draw a line AC, from A through the X, to point C.

              Make sure it is 4·5 centimetres long.

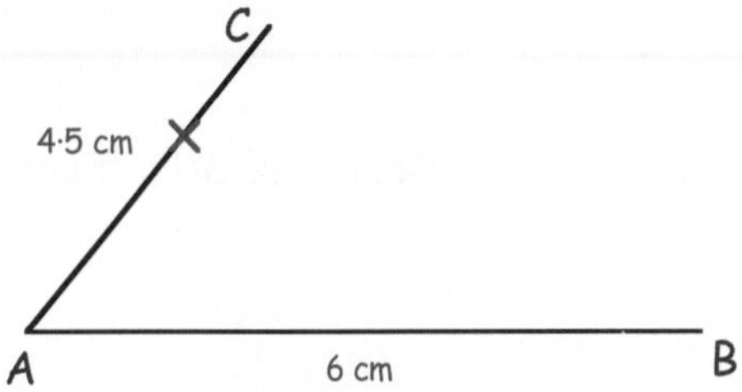

Step 4 :-   Join B to C to make the triangle.

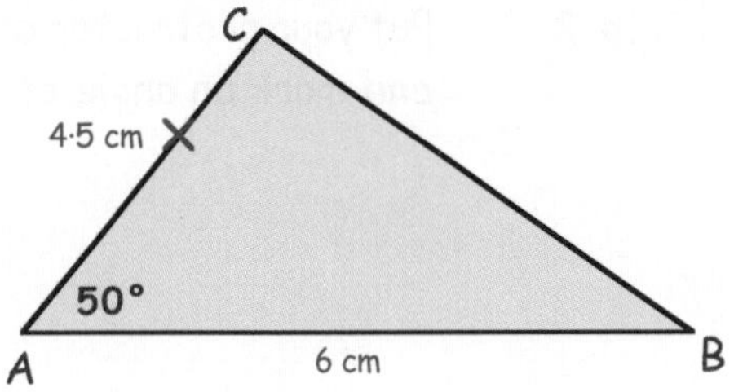

1. Shown is a sketch of ΔDEF.

   Follow the instructions to draw it accurately :-

   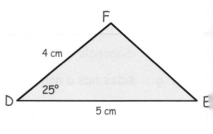

Step 1 :-	Draw line DE = 5 cm
Step 2 :-	Put your protractor at D and mark (with an X) an angle of 25°.
Step 3 :-	Draw line DF, from F through the X, to point F. *(Make sure it is 4 centimetres long)*.
Step 4 :-	Join E to F to make the triangle.

2. Make accurate drawings of the following triangles :-

   a 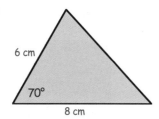   b 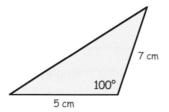   c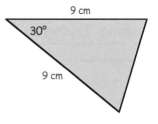

3. Make accurate drawings of the following triangles :-
   (Make rough sketches of the triangles first before drawing them accurately).

   a   Draw ΔKLM where   KL = 10 cm,   KM = 8 cm and ∠MKL = 60°.

   b   Draw ΔPUT where   PU = 11 cm,   UT = 6·5 cm and ∠PUT = 120°.

Two Angles and a Side

Shown opposite is a sketch of ΔSUD.

To draw it accurately :-

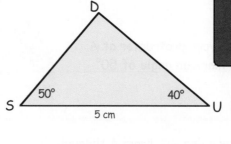

Given 2 angles and a side, be able to draw a triangle

Step 1 :-   Draw line SU = 5 cm

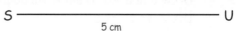

Step 2 :-   Put your protractor at S
            and mark an angle of 50°.

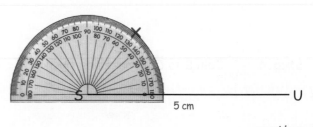

continued

Step 3 :- Draw line from S through the point X.

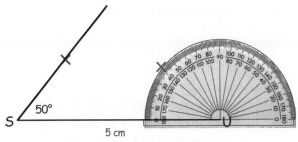

Step 4 :- Now put your protractor at U and mark an angle of 40°.

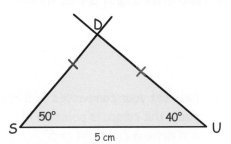

Step 5 :- Finally, draw the line from U through your new X point.

(Mark the point where the two lines meet with the letter D).

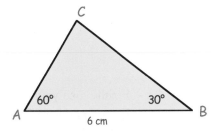

Exercise 3

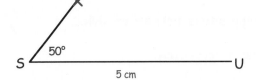

1. Shown is a sketch of △ABC.

   Follow the instructions to draw it accurately :-

Step 1 :-	Draw line AB = 6 cm
Step 2 :-	Put your protractor at A and mark (with an X) an angle of 60°.
Step 3 :-	Draw a line from A through the X.
Step 4 :-	Put your protractor at B and mark (with an X) an angle of 30°.
Step 5 :-	Draw a line from B through the X, to meet your first line at point C.

2. Make accurate drawings of these triangles :-

   a 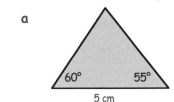   b 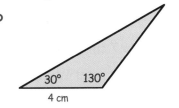   c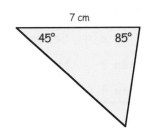

3. Make accurate drawings of the following triangles :-
   (Make rough sketches of the triangles first before drawing them accurately).

   a Draw △PLJ where   PL = 9 cm, ∠JPL = 55° and ∠PLJ = 65°.

   b Draw △HMV where   HM = 6 cm, ∠VHM = 120° and ∠HMV = 25°.

Three Sides

Shown opposite is a sketch of △NRZ.

To draw it accurately :-

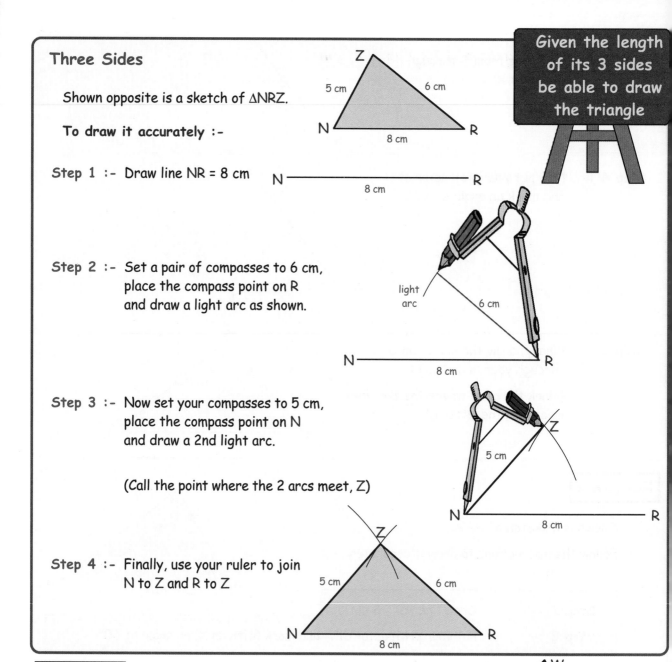

Step 1 :- Draw line NR = 8 cm

Step 2 :- Set a pair of compasses to 6 cm, place the compass point on R and draw a light arc as shown.

Step 3 :- Now set your compasses to 5 cm, place the compass point on N and draw a 2nd light arc.

(Call the point where the 2 arcs meet, Z)

Step 4 :- Finally, use your ruler to join N to Z and R to Z

Given the length of its 3 sides be able to draw the triangle

Exercise 4

1. Shown is a sketch of △POW.
   Draw it accurately using the following instructions :-

   Step 1 :- Draw line PO = 6 cm

   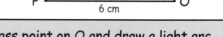

   Step 2 :- Set your compasses to 5 cm, place the compass point on O and draw a light arc.

   Step 3 :- Now set your compasses to 7 cm, place the compass point on P and draw a 2nd arc.

   Step 4 :- Call this point where the arcs meet W and join W to P and to O.

2. Make accurate drawings of these triangles :-

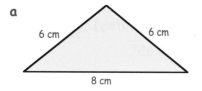

a   6 cm   6 cm   8 cm

b   8 cm   4 cm   5 cm

c   6 cm   6 cm   6 cm

Be able to draw quadrilaterals and regular polygons

Three examples using only a pair of compasses and a straight edge :-

Bisecting a Line at Right Angles

We want to find the midpoint of line AB.

Step 1 :-   Set your compasses to a size larger than half of AB.

Step 2 :-   Draw an arc, centre A and another arc, centre B, with same radius.

Step 3 :-   Join the 2 points (C and D) where the arcs intersect.

This line CD will bisect (cut in half) AB and does so at right angles. (*Discuss why*).

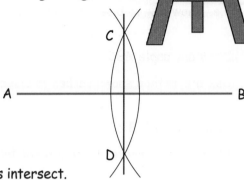

Bisecting an Angle

We want to cut ∠PUT in half (bisect it).

Step 1 :-   With centre U and using any radius, draw an arc, cutting PU at Q and UT at R.

Step 2 :-   With the same radius as above, draw an arc centre Q and another, centre R. These will meet at a point (call it X).

Step 3 :-   Join U to X. This line will cut ∠PUT in half.

Can you see that UQXR is a rhombus ? (*Discuss why this is so*).

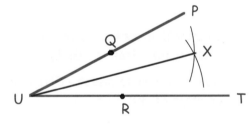

Drawing a 60° Angle

Step 1 :-   Draw a line KL.

Step 2 :-   With radius KL draw an arc centre K.

Step 3 :-   Draw a 2nd arc, centre L, with the same radius.

Step 4 :-   The 2 arcs intersect at a point M.

Join K to M. (∠MKL = 60°). (*Why ?*)

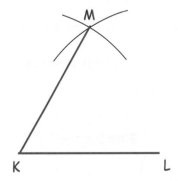

1. Draw a line PQ in your jotter and use a method
   shown on the previous page to find its **mid-point**.
   (i.e. show how to bisect the line PQ)

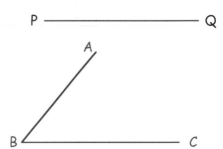

P ——————————— Q

2. Draw any angle ABC.

   Use the method shown earlier to **bisect** the angle.

3. Draw a line KP, 8 cm long.

   Show how to create an **equilateral triangle** KPR.

4. Draw a line CD = 7 cm and make an accurate drawing
   of rectangle CDEF sketched opposite :-

   (**No** protractor allowed here !)

5. 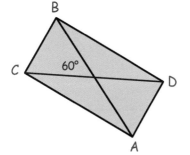 Draw the same line CD = 7 cm and create a rectangle,
   but this time the diagonal has to be 7 cm.

6. a Start with a line HI = 8 cm and create an
     angle of 60°. (call it ∠GHI).

   H ——————————— I
           8 cm

   b Now show how to **bisect** ∠GHI to create
     an angle of 30°.

7. Show how to create the rhombus KLMN
   shown opposite, using only a ruler
   and a pair of compasses.

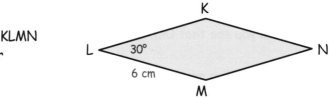

For Question 8 you can use compasses and a ruler - but a NOT a protractor !

8. Make accurate drawings of these two quadrilaterals :-

   a   b

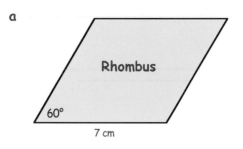

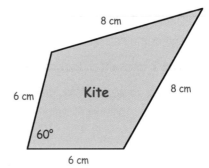

The 3 Я's

Revisit - Review - Revise

1. What is the **mathematical name** given to these **polygon** shapes ?

    a 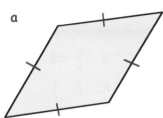   b   c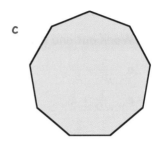

2. Make an accurate drawing of a **rectangle** with length 8 cm and breadth 5·5 cm.

3. a   Make an **accurate** drawing of **triangle** PQR.

    b   Measure and write down the size of line RQ.

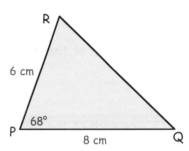

4. a   Draw accurately a **triangle** named DEF where :-

    DE = 8·5 cm   ∠DEF = 65°   ∠FDE = 25°.

    b   Measure and write down the size of line DF.

5. 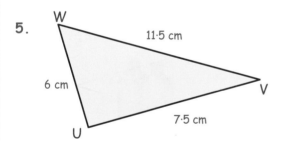   Look at the sketch of triangle UVW.

    a   Make an accurate drawing of this triangle.

    b   Measure and mark in the sizes of its angles.

6. Draw a **kite** with sides 5 cm, 5 cm, 8 cm and 8 cm.

    The angle between the 2 smaller sides is to be 110°.

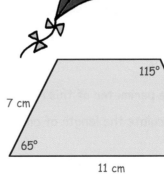

7. a   Make a neat, accurate drawing of this **trapezium**.

    b   Measure the length of the 4th side.

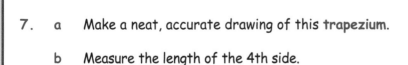

REVIEW 7

1. Write down two equivalent fractions for :-

   a $\frac{1}{3}$ b $\frac{3}{4}$ c $\frac{5}{8}$ d $\frac{3}{100}$.

2. Work out and simplify where possible :-

   a $\frac{3}{5} + \frac{1}{5}$ b $\frac{7}{8} - \frac{3}{8}$ c $\frac{1}{3} + \frac{1}{4}$ d $\frac{1}{6} + \frac{1}{5}$

   e $\frac{1}{10} + \frac{1}{2}$ f $\frac{1}{3} - \frac{1}{6}$ g $\frac{3}{4} + \frac{1}{3}$ h $\frac{4}{5} - \frac{1}{2}$

   i $\frac{3}{4} - \frac{2}{5}$ j $\frac{9}{10} - \frac{2}{3}$ k $1 - \frac{4}{5}$ l $\frac{13}{16} - \frac{5}{8}$.

3. Find :-   a $\frac{1}{3} + \frac{1}{4} + \frac{1}{5}$ b $\frac{3}{4} + \frac{1}{3} - \frac{2}{5}$ c $\frac{3}{5} + \frac{2}{3} - \frac{3}{4}$.

4. Change each of the following into a top heavy fraction :-

   a $2\frac{1}{5}$ b $1\frac{7}{8}$ c $3\frac{2}{7}$ d $5\frac{9}{10}$.

5. Change each of the following into a mixed number :-

   a $\frac{11}{4}$ b $\frac{20}{3}$ c $\frac{33}{5}$ d $\frac{40}{11}$.

6. Find each of the following, leaving your answer as a mixed number :-

   a $\frac{3}{2} + \frac{4}{3}$ b $2\frac{2}{5} + 1\frac{2}{5}$ c $5\frac{5}{6} - 1\frac{1}{6}$ d $3\frac{1}{4} + 4\frac{1}{5}$

   e $7\frac{1}{2} + 2\frac{3}{4}$ f $8\frac{3}{4} - 5\frac{5}{8}$ g $9\frac{7}{8} - 4\frac{1}{2}$ h $5\frac{2}{3} + 2\frac{3}{5}$

   i $6\frac{1}{4} - 4\frac{2}{3}$ j $10\frac{2}{7} - 8\frac{3}{4}$ k $7 - 3\frac{4}{9}$ l $15 - 12\frac{2}{5}$.

7. We took $4\frac{1}{2}$ litres of Cola with us on a picnic.

   On returning, we were left with $1\frac{2}{3}$ litres.

   How much Cola had we consumed ?

8.  Rod got his chain and his wife's bracelet valued for insurance purposes.

   His chain weighed $3\frac{2}{5}$ ounces and the bracelet weighed $1\frac{5}{8}$ ounces.

   What was the combined weight of the two pieces of jewellery ?

9. The perimeter of this rectangle is $18\frac{1}{6}$ cm.

   Calculate the length of one of its smaller sides.

   $5\frac{3}{4}$ cm

CHAPTER 8

Multiplying Fractions

Be able to multiply one fraction by another fraction

The rule for **multiplying** two basic fractions is very simple.

To multiply $\frac{3}{5} \times \frac{4}{7}$ $\longrightarrow$ $\frac{3}{5} \times \frac{4}{7} = \frac{3 \times 4}{5 \times 7} = \frac{12}{35}$

Example 1 :-

$\frac{3}{4} \times \frac{3}{5}$

$= \frac{3 \times 3}{4 \times 5}$

$= \frac{9}{20}$

Example 2 :-

$\frac{4}{5} \times \frac{5}{6}$

$= \frac{20}{30} \left(\frac{4 \times 5}{5 \times 6}\right)$

$= \frac{2}{3}$ (simplified)

Example 3 :-

$\frac{8}{9} \times \frac{3}{4}$

$= \frac{24}{36}$

$= \frac{2}{3}$

Basic Rule :-

- Multiply the 2 numerators.
- Multiply the 2 denominators.
- Simplify where possible.

Exercise 1

1. Copy each of the following and complete :-

   a $\quad \frac{3}{4} \times \frac{4}{5}$

   $= \frac{3 \times 4}{4 \times 5}$

   $= \frac{?}{20} = \frac{?}{?}$

   b $\quad \frac{5}{6} \times \frac{1}{3}$

   $= \frac{5 \times 1}{6 \times 3}$

   $= \frac{?}{?}$

   c $\quad \frac{3}{4} \times \frac{5}{6}$

   $= \frac{3 \times 5}{4 \times 6}$

   $= \frac{15}{24} = \frac{?}{8}.$

2. Multiply the following fractions and simplify (where possible) :-

   a $\quad \frac{4}{5} \times \frac{2}{3}$

   b $\quad \frac{5}{6} \times \frac{7}{10}$

   c $\quad \frac{3}{5} \times \frac{4}{9}$

   d $\quad \frac{4}{7} \times \frac{5}{6}$

   e $\quad \frac{5}{8} \times \frac{4}{5}$

   f $\quad \frac{7}{12} \times \frac{6}{7}$

   g $\quad \frac{11}{16} \times \frac{2}{3}$

   h $\quad \frac{2}{9} \times \frac{9}{10}$

   i $\quad \frac{4}{5} \times \frac{3}{5} \times \frac{1}{2}$

   j $\quad \frac{4}{7} \times \frac{3}{8} \times \frac{1}{2}$

   k $\quad \frac{3}{10} \times \frac{3}{5} \times \frac{3}{8}$

   l $\quad \frac{5}{6} \times \frac{2}{5} \times \frac{11}{16}.$

3. Calculate the **area** of a rectangular sheet of metal measuring $\frac{5}{6}$ metre by $\frac{3}{8}$ metre.

4. I spent $\frac{3}{4}$ of my paper round wage in a shop. Of that, $\frac{2}{5}$ of it went on sweets.

   What fraction of my wage was spent on sweets ? (i.e. $\frac{2}{5} \times \frac{3}{4}$).

5.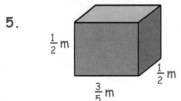

   $\frac{1}{2}$ m $\frac{1}{2}$ m $\frac{3}{5}$ m

   A cuboid has dimensions as shown.

   Find the volume of this cuboid in cubic metres.

Dealing with Mixed Fractions :- $(3\frac{1}{2} \times 2\frac{1}{3})$

Simple Rule :-   You MUST CHANGE mixed fractions into top-heavy fractions first.

Example 4 :-

$3\frac{1}{2} \times 2\frac{1}{3}$

$= \frac{7}{2} \times \frac{7}{3}$

$= \frac{49}{6}$

$= 8\frac{1}{6}$

Example 5 :-

$4\frac{3}{4} \times 1\frac{1}{3}$

$= \frac{19}{4} \times \frac{4}{3}$

$= \frac{76}{12}$

$= \frac{19}{3} = 6\frac{1}{3}$

6.   Copy and complete the following :-

a

$3\frac{1}{2} \times 1\frac{1}{3}$

$= \frac{7}{2} \times \frac{4}{3}$

$= \frac{28}{6}$

$= 4\frac{...}{6} \quad = 4\frac{...}{...}$

b

$5\frac{2}{3} \times 1\frac{1}{4}$

$= \frac{17}{3} \times \frac{5}{4}$

$= \frac{85}{12}$

$= 7\frac{...}{...}$

c

$2\frac{2}{3} \times 1\frac{3}{4}$

$= \frac{...}{3} \times \frac{...}{4}$

$= \frac{...}{12}$

$= 4\frac{...}{...} \quad = 4\frac{...}{...}$.

7.   Do the following fractions in the same way (*simplify wherever possible*) :-

a $3\frac{1}{3} \times 2\frac{1}{2}$

b $3\frac{1}{5} \times 3\frac{1}{2}$

c $4\frac{1}{3} \times 1\frac{3}{4}$

d $1\frac{2}{7} \times 3\frac{2}{3}$

e $2\frac{1}{4} \times 1\frac{3}{5}$

f $1\frac{5}{6} \times 4\frac{1}{2}$

g $3\frac{3}{10} \times 2\frac{1}{3}$

h $1\frac{1}{2} \times 1\frac{2}{5}$

i $3\frac{2}{3} \times 1\frac{3}{4}$

j $4\frac{1}{2} \times 2\frac{4}{5}$

k $3\frac{1}{2} \times 10\frac{6}{7}$

l $6\frac{1}{2} \times \frac{4}{5}$.

8.   A rectangular piece of metal measures $1\frac{1}{3}$ inches wide by $4\frac{1}{2}$ inches long.

Calculate its area.

(*note   " - is the old symbol used to stand for "inch".*)

$1\frac{1}{3}$ "

$4\frac{1}{2}$ "

9.   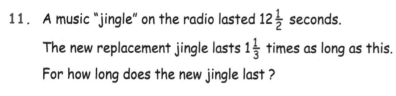 A one metre length of a kitchen worktop weighs $3\frac{3}{4}$ kg.

What would a $2\frac{1}{2}$ metre length of the worktop weigh ?

10.   Alice's mum found that she weighed $1\frac{2}{3}$ times as much as Alice.

If Alice weighed $31\frac{1}{2}$ kilograms, what did her mum weigh ?

11.   A music "jingle" on the radio lasted $12\frac{1}{2}$ seconds.

The new replacement jingle lasts $1\frac{1}{3}$ times as long as this.

For how long does the new jingle last ?

12.   Find the volume of a cuboid with dimensions $\frac{1}{4}$ m by $\frac{2}{3}$ m by $1\frac{1}{2}$ m.

Division of Fractions

It is almost impossible to divide fractions like $(\frac{2}{3} \div \frac{3}{5})$ normally.

=> Instead, we change a "division" problem to a "multiplication" one.

=> $\frac{2}{3} \div \frac{3}{5}$ is the same as $\dfrac{\frac{2}{3}}{\frac{3}{5}}$

=> We can simplify the denominator by multiplying both it and the numerator, by $\frac{5}{3}$.

$\dfrac{\frac{2}{3}}{\frac{3}{5}}$ becomes $\dfrac{\frac{2}{3} \times (\frac{5}{3})}{\frac{3}{5} \times (\frac{5}{3})}$

$= \dfrac{\frac{10}{9}}{\frac{15}{15}} = \dfrac{\frac{10}{9}}{1} = \frac{10}{9} = 1\frac{1}{9}$

Since $\dfrac{\frac{5}{3}}{\frac{5}{3}} = 1$, this does not alter the answer.

This becomes easier if we miss out the bottom line which always becomes 1.

$\frac{2}{3} \div \frac{3}{5}$ becomes $\boxed{\frac{2}{3} \times \frac{5}{3}} = \frac{10}{9} = 1\frac{1}{9}$.

* Rule :- instead of dividing by $\frac{a}{b}$, => multiply by $\frac{b}{a}$ instead.

Example :- $\frac{5}{8} \div \frac{2}{3} = \frac{5}{8} \times \frac{3}{2} = \frac{15}{16}$.

Exercise 2

1. Copy each of the following and complete :-

   a
   $\frac{3}{4} \div \frac{3}{10}$

   $= \frac{3}{4} \times \frac{10}{3}$

   $= \frac{?}{12} = \frac{?}{4} = 2\frac{?}{?}$

   b
   $\frac{1}{6} \div \frac{2}{3}$

   $= \frac{1}{6} \times \frac{3}{2}$

   $= \frac{?}{12} = \frac{?}{?}$

   c
   $\frac{3}{4} \div \frac{5}{6}$

   $= \frac{3}{4} \times \frac{6}{5}$

   $= \frac{?}{20} = \frac{?}{?}$.

2. Divide the following fractions and simplify (where possible) :-

   a $\frac{2}{5} \div \frac{2}{9}$ b $\frac{5}{6} \div \frac{5}{12}$ c $\frac{3}{7} \div \frac{6}{7}$ d $\frac{3}{5} \div \frac{4}{5}$

   e $\frac{5}{12} \div \frac{5}{6}$ f $\frac{7}{12} \div \frac{7}{8}$ g $\frac{11}{16} \div \frac{5}{8}$ h $\frac{2}{9} \div \frac{1}{6}$

   i $\frac{5}{9} \div \frac{3}{5}$ j $\frac{7}{16} \div \frac{3}{10}$ k $\frac{8}{9} \div \frac{3}{4}$ l $\frac{1}{5} \div \frac{1}{7}$.

3. a How many $\frac{3}{10}$'s are there in $\frac{2}{5}$'s ?

   b How many pieces of cloth $\frac{1}{16}$ metre long, can I cut from a piece $\frac{3}{4}$ metre long ?

Division of Mixed Fractions :- $(3\frac{1}{2} \div 2\frac{1}{3})$

Rule :-
- You **MUST CHANGE** mixed fractions to be top-heavy fractions first,
- then use the rule "turn the 2nd fraction upside down and multiply".

Example 1 :-

$$3\frac{1}{2} \div 2\frac{1}{3}$$
$$= \frac{7}{2} \div \frac{7}{3}$$
$$= \frac{7}{2} \times \frac{3}{7}$$
$$= \frac{21}{14} = 1\frac{7}{14} = 1\frac{1}{2}$$

Example 2 :-

$$5\frac{3}{4} \div 1\frac{2}{3}$$
$$= \frac{23}{4} \div \frac{5}{3}$$
$$= \frac{23}{4} \times \frac{3}{5}$$
$$= \frac{69}{20} = 3\frac{9}{20}$$

4. Copy and complete the following :-

a
$$2\frac{1}{4} \div 1\frac{1}{5}$$
$$= \frac{9}{4} \div \frac{6}{5}$$
$$= \frac{9}{4} \times \frac{?}{6}$$
$$= \ldots = \ldots$$

b
$$4\frac{2}{3} \div 1\frac{2}{5}$$
$$= \frac{14}{3} \div \frac{7}{5}$$
$$= \frac{14}{3} \times \frac{?}{?}$$
$$= \ldots = \ldots$$

c
$$2\frac{2}{3} \div 3\frac{1}{5}$$
$$= \frac{?}{3} \div \frac{?}{5}$$
$$= \ldots$$
$$= \ldots = \ldots$$

5. Divide the following fractions in the same way (simplify if possible) :-

a $4\frac{1}{3} \div 1\frac{1}{2}$ b $4\frac{1}{5} \div 3\frac{1}{2}$ c $2\frac{1}{3} \div 1\frac{3}{4}$ d $3\frac{3}{7} \div 2\frac{2}{3}$

e $2\frac{1}{4} \div 1\frac{3}{5}$ f $7\frac{1}{2} \div 1\frac{1}{4}$ g $1\frac{3}{5} \div 3\frac{2}{3}$ h $17\frac{1}{2} \div 1\frac{3}{7}$

i $5\frac{1}{3} \div 1\frac{3}{5}$ j $9\frac{1}{2} \div 1\frac{1}{4}$ k $6 \div 2\frac{1}{2}$ l $8 \div \frac{2}{3}$.

6. The area of this piece of card is $10\frac{1}{2}$ square inches.
   It is $1\frac{2}{3}$ inches wide. Calculate its length.

 $1\frac{2}{3}$ " | **Area** = $10\frac{1}{2}$ square inches

7. A $4\frac{1}{2}$ metre length of guttering weighs $10\frac{1}{8}$ kilograms.

   a   What does 1 metre of the guttering weigh ?

   b   What is the weight of a $1\frac{1}{4}$ metre guttering ?

8. My fir tree is $1\frac{3}{4}$ times as tall my elm tree.

   If my fir tree is $4\frac{1}{4}$ metres tall, how tall is my elm tree ?

9.  $2\frac{1}{4}$ laps of the park took Mr Bridger $12\frac{1}{2}$ minutes to walk.

   How long, on average, did each lap take ?

Mixed Exercise using all 4 operators.

1. Change to a mixed number :-   a $\frac{24}{5}$ b $\frac{42}{8}$.

2. Rewrite as a top-heavy fraction :-   a $4\frac{5}{6}$ b $10\frac{2}{7}$.

3. How many $\frac{1}{3}$ pizza slices can by sold from $6\frac{2}{3}$ pizzas ?

4. Copy and complete :-

    a $\frac{3}{7} + \frac{2}{7}$ b $\frac{1}{2} + \frac{3}{4}$ c $\frac{5}{6} - \frac{1}{6}$ d $2\frac{3}{5} + 1\frac{4}{5}$

    e $7\frac{3}{5} - 5\frac{1}{3}$ f $7\frac{1}{2} - \frac{2}{3}$ g $11\frac{7}{8} - 9\frac{2}{3}$ h $11\frac{2}{3} - 10\frac{11}{12}$.

5. Copy and complete :-

    a $\frac{1}{2} \times \frac{1}{3}$ b $\frac{8}{9} \times \frac{3}{5}$ c $3\frac{1}{2} \times 2\frac{1}{5}$ d $\frac{5}{8} \div \frac{1}{4}$

    e $\frac{11}{12} \div \frac{2}{5}$ f $3\frac{3}{4} \div 2\frac{2}{3}$ g $13\frac{1}{2} \div 1\frac{4}{5}$ h $\frac{1}{4} \div 2\frac{1}{4}$.

6. Before her diet, Mrs Barbour weighed $11\frac{1}{2}$ stones.

    She lost $2\frac{3}{4}$ stones on her diet.

    What was her new weight ?

7.  A hardware shop sells lengths of heavy duty chain.

    1 metre of the chain weighs $2\frac{4}{5}$ kg.

    What will the weight of a $1\frac{1}{4}$ metre chain be ?

8. An empty wooden crate weighs $4\frac{7}{8}$ kg.

    It holds 6 large cartons of rice.

    Each carton weighs $1\frac{3}{4}$ kg.

    Calculate the total weight of the crate and cartons.

9.  $1\frac{1}{3}$ cm

    The area of this rectangle is $7\frac{1}{5}$ cm².

    Its breadth is $1\frac{1}{3}$ cm.

    Calculate its length.

10. Find :- $\frac{1}{2} \times \frac{2}{3} \times \frac{3}{4} \times \frac{4}{5} \times \frac{5}{6} \times \frac{6}{7} \times \frac{7}{8}$.

1. Change to a mixed number :-

   a $\frac{17}{4}$

   b $\frac{49}{9}$

   c $\frac{121}{2}$

   d $\frac{67}{7}$.

2. Rewrite as a top-heavy fraction :-

   a $1\frac{5}{6}$

   b $8\frac{2}{7}$

   c $5\frac{2}{3}$

   d $11\frac{7}{9}$.

3. How many $\frac{1}{3}$ pizza slices can by sold from $4\frac{2}{3}$ pizzas ?

4. Multiply the following fractions and simplify fully (where possible) :-

   a $\frac{4}{5} \times \frac{2}{3}$

   b $\frac{5}{8} \times \frac{7}{10}$

   c $\frac{3}{5} \times \frac{5}{9}$

   d $\frac{5}{7} \times \frac{3}{5} \times \frac{1}{2}$

   e $2\frac{1}{3} \times 4\frac{1}{2}$

   f $3\frac{1}{5} \times 1\frac{1}{2}$

   g $7\frac{1}{3} \times 3\frac{3}{4}$

   h $7\frac{1}{2} \times \frac{4}{5}$.

5. Divide the following fractions and simplify fully (where possible) :-

   a $\frac{2}{3} \div \frac{2}{9}$

   b $\frac{5}{6} \div \frac{5}{12}$

   c $\frac{3}{14} \div \frac{6}{7}$

   d $\frac{3}{5} \div \frac{4}{5}$

   e $2\frac{1}{3} \div 3\frac{1}{2}$

   f $4\frac{1}{5} \div 1\frac{1}{2}$

   g $3\frac{1}{3} \div 2\frac{3}{4}$

   h $5 \div \frac{2}{3}$.

6. a Calculate the area of a rectangle measuring $4\frac{1}{4}$ cm by $1\frac{3}{5}$ cm.

   b How many $\frac{1}{3}$ metre lengths of wood can I cut from a $10\frac{1}{2}$ metre length ?

   c Mia 's mum weighs $3\frac{1}{2}$ times as much as Mia, who weighs $16\frac{3}{4}$ kg.
   What is the weight of her mum ?

7. a A cube has each of its sides $3\frac{1}{3}$ cm.
   Calculate the volume of the cuboid.

   b A square has side $2\frac{2}{3}$ centimetres.

   A rectangle has a perimeter with the same numerical
   value as the area of the square.

   The rectangle has length equal to three times its breadth.

   Find the length of the rectangle.

REVIEW 8

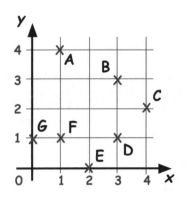

Coordinates

1. Write down the coordinates of all the points :-

   a   from A to G

   b   that have the same y coordinate

   c   that have the same x coordinate

   d   that have the same x and y coordinate

   e   3 along and 2 up from G

   f   3 back and 1 down from B.

2. Copy the coordinate grid above and plot the following points :-

   L(4, 3),   M(2, 4),   N(0, 3),   O(0, 0),   P(3, 4),   Q(2, 1·5).

3. a   Write down all the coordinates from Q to Z.

   b   Write down all the points that have the same y coordinate.

   c   Write down all the points that have the same x and y coordinate.

   d   TVZA are the vertices of a rectangle.
       State the coordinates of A.

   e   YZUB are the vertices of a parallelogram.
       State the coordinates of B.

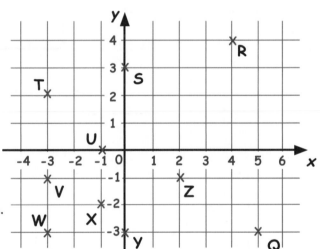

4. a   Draw a set of axes (from –5 to 5).

   b   Plot the following points on your grid :-
       C(5, 3),   D(-1, 5),   E(-3, -1),   F(4, -2),   G(-5, 0),   H(0, -4),   I(-5, -5).

5. a   Draw a set of axes (from –5 to 5).

   b   Plot the triangle with vertices of P(0, 4), Q(4, 3) and R(5, –2).

   c   Reflect triangle PQR over the :-   (i)   the y axis   (ii)   x axis.

6. Repeat question 5a and 5c for the quadrilateral with vertices :-

   M(–4, –3),   N(–3, 1),   O(0, 0)   and   P(1, –3).

CHAPTER 9

Scale Drawing and Bearings

Enlarging & Reducing Shapes

If you are asked to make a **two-times enlargement** of a shape, simply **double** all of its sizes.

e.g. a rectangle measuring 3 cm by 6 cm will become a 6 cm by 12 cm rectangle.

Similarly, if a **three times reduction** is made on the 3 cm by 6 cm rectangle, it will become a 1 cm by 2 cm rectangle, (÷3).

Exercise 1

1. Make a **two-times enlargement** of these shapes, each large box being 1 cm by 1 cm.

a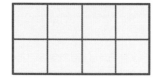

b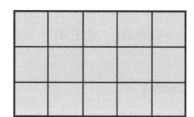

c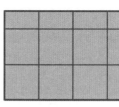

d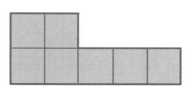

e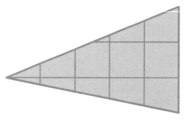

f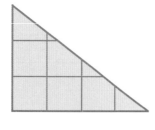

g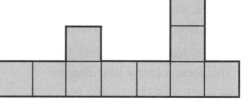

h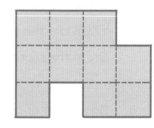

i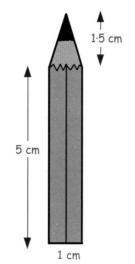

j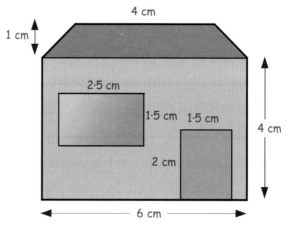

2. Make enlargements of the following using the given scale :-

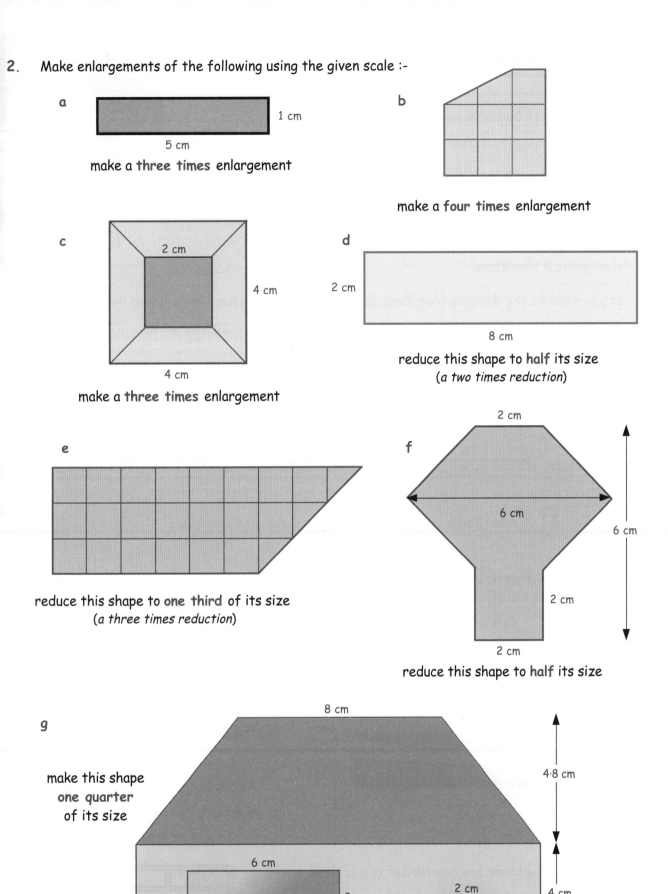

a

1 cm

5 cm

make a **three times** enlargement

b

make a **four times** enlargement

c

2 cm

4 cm

4 cm

make a **three times** enlargement

d

2 cm

8 cm

reduce this shape to **half** its size
(*a two times reduction*)

e

reduce this shape to **one third** of its size
(*a three times reduction*)

f

2 cm

6 cm

6 cm

2 cm

2 cm

reduce this shape to **half** its size

g

make this shape
one quarter
of its size

8 cm

4·8 cm

6 cm

2 cm

2 cm

2 cm

4 cm

2 cm

1 cm

2 cm

2 cm

16 cm

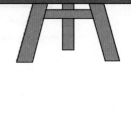

This is a map of Durah Island, drawn to scale.

It has been drawn to a scale of :-

$$1\,cm = 8\,km.$$

What this simply means is that every time you measure 1 cm on the diagram, in real life it represents 8 kilometres.

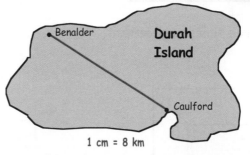

1 cm = 8 km

If you measure the distance from Benalder to Caulford on the map, you will find it is 4 centimetres.

=>   the real distance between the 2 towns is 4 x 8 = 32 kilometres.

> RULE :-   To find the real distance between 2 places :-
>
> • Measure the distance on the map using a ruler,
>
> • Multiply your measurement by the "scale" value.

Exercise 2   *A ruler and a calculator are required for ALL exercises.*

1.   This scale drawing of Mr Able's allotment is drawn to a scale of :-

$$1\,cm = 4\,m.$$

a   Calculate the real length of the allotment.

b   Now calculate its real breadth.

3 cm

Mr Able's Allotment

8·5 cm

2.

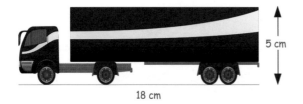

5 cm

18 cm

This truck has been drawn using the scale :-

$$1\,cm = 1\cdot5\,m.$$

a   Calculate the real length of the truck.

b   Calculate its real height.

3.   This window frame has been drawn to a scale of :-

1 cm represents 20 cm.

a   Calculate the real length of the window.

b   Calculate the real height of the window.

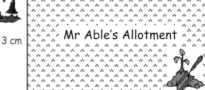

9·5 cm

5·5 cm

4. This drawing of a garden gate is done using a scale :-

   1 cm represents 25 cm.

   Calculate :-

   a   the real width of the gate.

   b   the real height of the gate.

   c   the real length of the diagonal support bar.

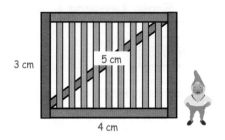

5.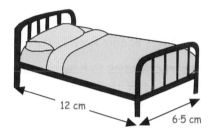

   This bed has been drawn to a scale of :-

   1 cm represents 18 cm.

   a   Calculate the real length of the bed.

   b   Calculate the real width of the bed.

6. Shown is a scale drawing of Florida Line-dance Hall.

   The scale is :-   1 : 400. (i.e. 1 cm = 400 cm = 4 m).

   a   Measure the length and breadth of
        the dance hall with your ruler.

   b   What is the real length and breadth of
        the hall, in metres.

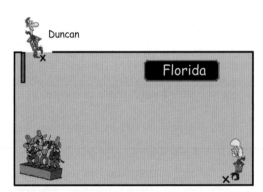

   c   Duncan enters by the door and heads straight towards Maisie, dancing in the far corner.

        How many metres has Duncan to walk ?

7.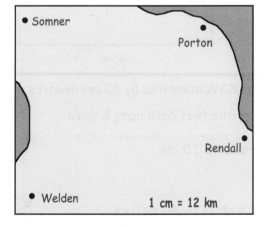

   The map opposite shows 4 islands in a
   stretch of water between two countries.

   a   Use your ruler to measure the distance
        from Somner to Welden.

   b   Use the scale of the map to work out the
        real distance between the 2 islands.

   c   Measure the distance between the following
        pairs of islands and then use the given scale
        to calculate the real distance between them :-

        (i)   Somner and Rendall

        (ii)   Porton and Welden.

Exercise 3

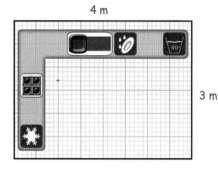

4 m

3 m

1. Here is a sketch of a kitchen.

   Make an accurate scale drawing of the kitchen using the simple scale of :-

   1 cm = 1 metre.

2.

30 m

21 m

This is a sketch of the Brodie Park Putting Green.

Below are the instructions as to how to make an accurate scale drawing of the putting green using a scale of :-

   1 : 300. (i.e. 1 cm = 300 cm = ... m).

a   If 3 metres is represented by 1 centimetre in the scale drawing

   =>   30 metres (length) will be represented by (30 ÷ 3) = 10 centimetres.

   Start your scale drawing by drawing a line 10 centimetres long.

b   Also   => 21 metres (breadth) will be represented by (21 ÷ 3) = ... cm.

   Now finish your scale drawing by drawing the width .... centimetres long and completing the rectangular putting green.

3. This car park measures 25 metres by 45 metres.

   Make a scale drawing of the car park using a scale :-

   1 cm represents 5 m.

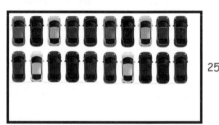

25 m

45 m

4.

The foot bath measures 80 centimetres by 60 centimetres.

Make a scale drawing of the foot bath using a scale :-

   1 cm represents 10 cm.

5. This light aircraft runway at Leuchars measures 240 metres by 40 metres.

   The scale is *1 : 2000.*

   a   What does 1 cm represent in metres ?

   b   Make a scale drawing of the runway.

240 m

40 m

6. a   Make a scale drawing to show this 12 m tall tower as it is
        viewed from point A, 5 metres from the base of the tower.

    The scale is **1 cm = 2 m.**

    b   Measure the length from point A
        to the top of the tower.

    c   What is the **real** length from point A
        to the top of the tower ?

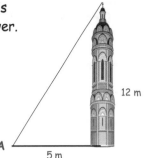

12 m

A _____ 5 m

7.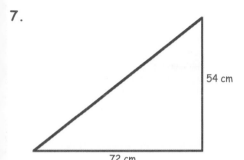

    54 cm

    72 cm

    The wooden roof support for a shed is shown.

    It is in the shape of a right angled triangle.

    a   Make a scale drawing of the support,
        using the scale :-

        1 cm represents 9 cm.

    b   Measure the sloping line on your drawing
        and calculate the **real** length of the sloping roof
        to the nearest centimetre.

8. A house has an "L-shaped" living room.

    Not all of the actual sizes of the room are shown.

    a   Write down the two sizes which are missing.

    b   Make a scale drawing of the room, using
        the scale :-

        1 cm represents 3 m.

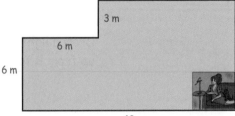

3 m

6 m

6 m

18 m

9.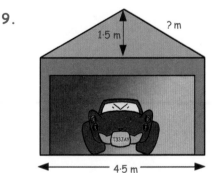

    ? m

    1·5 m

    4·5 m

    The blue garage roof is in the shape of an isosceles triangle.

    a   Make a scale drawing of the roof using a scale :-

        1 : 50   (What does 1 cm represent in metres) ?

    b   Measure one of the sloping lines and calculate the
        real length of the sloping garage roof on one side.

10. Here is a sketch of the door side of another garden shed.

    Make a scale drawing of it, including the door,
    using the scale :-

        1 cm represents 25 cm.

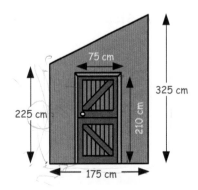

75 cm

325 cm

225 cm

210 cm

175 cm

A ruler and a protractor are required for this exercise.

Example :-

The sketch shows a flagpole supported by a wire (AC).

The distance from A to B is 16 metres and ∠BAC = 50°.

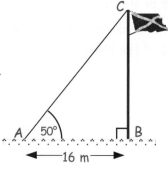

1. Follow the instructions below **carefully** in order to make an accurate scale drawing using a scale of :-

    1 cm = 2 metres.

2. Use your drawing to calculate the **real** height of the flagpole.

    Step 1 :-   Scale   2 m = 1 cm

    => 16 m becomes (16 ÷ 2) = 8 cm.

    => draw AB = 8 cm

    Step 2 :-   Draw a light line straight up from B to show the flagpole.

    light line

    Step 3 :-   Put your protractor on A and mark out an angle of 50°.

    Step 4 :-   Draw the 50° line from A till it crosses the line drawn up from B.

    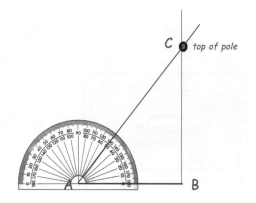

    C ● *top of pole*

    Step 5 :-   Measure the length from B to C, where the 2 lines cross (in cm).

    Step 6 :-   Multiply this length by the scale (x 2) to obtain the real height of the flagpole in metres.

    BC = 9·5 cm

    Real height of pole = 9·5 x 2 = 19 m

1. a   Make a scale drawing to show this tree as it is viewed from point P.

    Use a scale of :- **1 cm = 2 metres**

    - Start by drawing the line representing PQ.

    - Draw a feint line straight up from Q.

    - Use your protractor to measure out ∠P = 40°.

    - Complete the drawing.

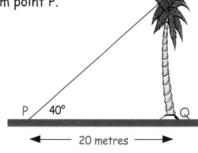

    b   Measure, in centimetres, the height of the tree in your drawing.

    c   Calculate the height of the **real** tree.

2. James is standing 18 metres from the medieval building tower.

    The angle between James' feet and the top of the tower is 60°.

    a   Make a scale drawing of the sketch.

                scale :- **1 cm = 3 metres**

    b   Calculate the height of the **real** tower.

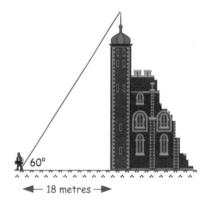

3. For each of the following :-

    (i)   Make a scale drawing using the given scale.

    (ii) Calculate the **real** height of the given object.

a
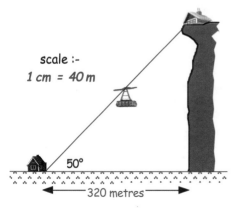
scale :-
1 cm = 5 m

b
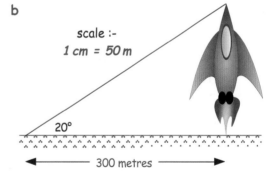
scale :-
1 cm = 50 m

c
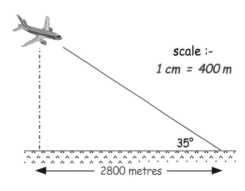
scale :-
1 cm = 40 m

d
scale :-
1 cm = 400 m

4. The picture shows a photographer bravely
    taking photos of a giant alien cowboy.

    a   Draw a triangle using the scale :-

            1 cm = 2 metres.

    b   Measure the height of the alien
        in your figure and calculate
        its real height.

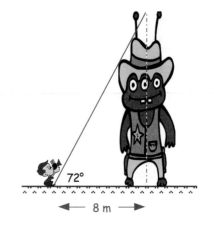

72°

←— 8 m —→

5.

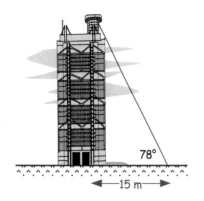

78°

←—15 m—→

Shown is one of the modern buildings on
the main street in the village of Brimley.

a   Make a scale drawing to represent
    the height of the building, using a scale :-

        1 cm = 2·5 m.

b   Measure the height of the building
    in your scale drawing and calculate
    its real height.

6. The sketch shows the journey a cargo ship
    makes when it delivers supplies to the islands.

    Yoar Island is due West of the Mainland
    and Boar Island is South of Yoar.

    a   Draw a triangle to scale, showing
        the ship's journey.

            scale 1 cm = 1·5 km.

    b   Measure the distance between the
        two islands in centimetres and calculate
        the real distance between them in kilometres.

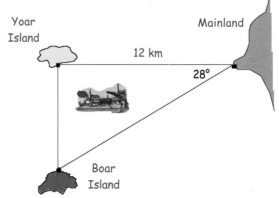

Yoar
Island

Mainland

12 km

28°

Boar
Island

7.

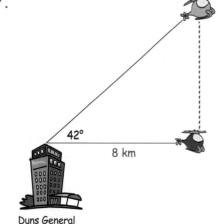

42°

8 km

Duns General

Two helicopters set off from the roof of Duns Hospital.

One of them heads off on a course due East.

The sketch shows where they are after 10 minutes.

The 2nd helicopter is now due North of the 1st one.

A scale of 1 : 100 000 is to be used to represent it.

a   How many kilometres does 1 cm represent ?

b   Make a scale drawing showing the paths
    of both helicopters.

c   Calculate how far apart the two aircraft
    are at the end of the 10 minutes.

Scale Drawings Involving Bearings

A ruler and a protractor are required for this exercise.

You should already know :-

- the points of a compass and their 3 figure bearings
- that bearings are measured clockwise from the North and always have 3 figures
- how to read bearings and measure them using a protractor.

Later in this exercise we combine all three to make scale drawings involving directions and bearings.

Exercise 5

1. Write down in which direction you end up heading when travelling :-

   a   North, then make a 45° turn clockwise.

   b   South East, then make a 90° turn clockwise.

   c   South, then make a 225° turn anti-clockwise.

   d   North West, then make a 315° anti-clockwise.

2. Write each of the following compass directions as a 3 figure bearing :-

   a   South   b   North East   c   West   d   South East

   e   North   f   East   g   North West   h   South West.

3. For each of these directions, write down its 3 figure bearing :-

   a   b   c
   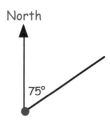   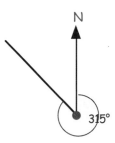   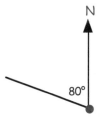

4. Using a protractor, measure and write down the 3 figure bearing for these directions :-

   a   b   c
   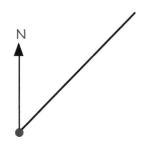      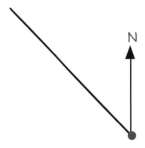

5. Use your protractor to draw a **3 figure bearing** of :-

   a   090°   b   140°   c   230°   d   310°.

6. A cruise liner and a tall-ship leave port (P) at the same time.

The cruise liner travels 60 kilometres north east.

The tall-ship sails 30 kilometres south east.

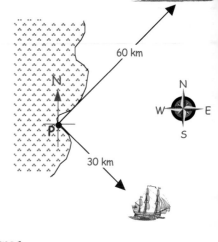

  a Make a scale drawing of the two journeys.

>   scale   *1 cm = 10 km*

> - start by marking a point on your page to show P
> - draw in the north-south and east-west lines through P
> - use your protractor to show 45° from north ie N.E.
> - use your ruler to show the cruise liner's journey path
> - repeat for the tall-ship's journey

  b Measure the distance between the two ships, in centimetres.

  c Now calculate the **real** distance between them, in kilometres.

7.

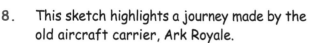

Two holiday flights leave Los Angeles Airport in USA.

One flies East for 200 kilometres.

The other flies South West for 280 kilometres.

  a Make a scale drawing of both flights.

>   scale *1 cm = 40 km*

  b Measure the distance between the two planes, in centimetres.

  c Now calculate the **real** distance between the two planes, in kilometres.

8. This sketch highlights a journey made by the old aircraft carrier, Ark Royale.

It sailed for 35 km on a bearing of 050° from Bearl Harbour to Mogri Island.

From there, it sailed on a bearing of 120° for 30 km to Habana.

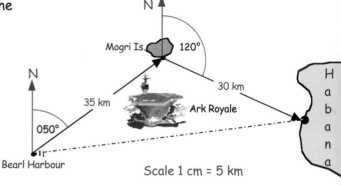

  a Make a scale drawing showing this route taken by the Ark Royale.

  b Measure the distance from Bearl Harbour to Habana on your scale drawing.

  c Calculate the distance the ship had to travel to return to Bearl Harbour from Habana.

9. An orienteer begins a competition by heading off on a bearing of 070° towards Checkpoint 1.

When he arrives, on what bearing must he then set off in to return directly to his starting point ?

Revisit - Review - Revise

1. Write the 3 figure bearing representing :-

    a   South West   b   South East   c   North East.

2.
    A toy school bus has been made to a scale :-   1 cm to 1·5 m.

    If the length of the toy bus is 6 cm, what is the length
    of the real school bus ?

3. The scale drawing shows the relative position of two petrol stations on a motorway.

    a   Measure the distance between them on the drawing.

    b   The scale of the drawing is :-   1 : 100 000.

    Calculate the real distance between
    the petrol stations, in kilometres.

4. a   Make a scale drawing of this sketch of a lighthouse.

    Scale - 1 cm - 20 metres

    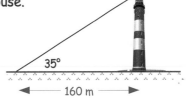
    35°
    ← 160 m →

    b   Determine the real height of the lighthouse.

5. A helicopter is used to take patients from a medical centre on a
    small island to the hospital on the mainland.

    The bearing of the hospital from the medical centre is 060°.

    What is the bearing of the medical centre from the hospital ? *(a sketch should help)*

6. A ship leaves Denham Harbour.

    It sails for 90 kilometres on a
    bearing of 055° to Buick Island.

    It then sails from Buick Island for 60 km
    on a bearing of 135° to Capa Point.

    a   Make a scale drawing showing
        the two stages of the trip.

            scale 1 cm = 10 km.

    b   Measure the distance from Denham
        Harbour to Capa Point in centimetres.

    c   Calculate the real distance from Denham Harbour to Capa Point, in kilometres.

    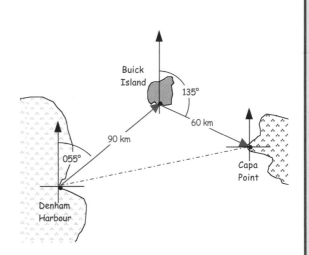

7. Draw a neat **2** times enlargement of this shape.

   Each box is a 1 centimetre square.

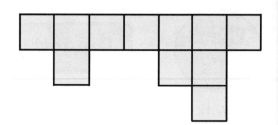

8.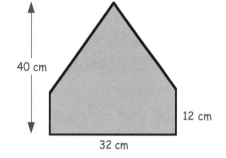

   This shape is not drawn to scale.

   Make an accurate drawing of the shape with one quarter of its given dimensions.

   40 cm

   12 cm

   32 cm

9. This cathedral has been drawn with a scale of :-

   1 cm represents 12 metres.

   Find the height of the real cathedral.

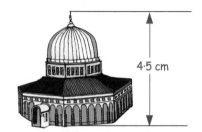

   4·5 cm

10.

    A model of a dinosaur is to be built $\frac{1}{500}$ of its real life size.

    The actual dinosaur is 15 metres tall.

    What will the height of the model be, in centimetres ?

11. What must the **reduction scale factor** have been in this diagram ?

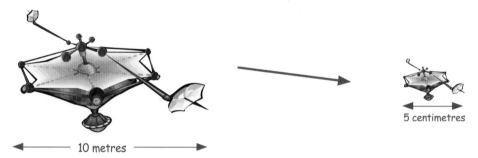

    10 metres

    5 centimetres

12. A photograph is taken of this scarecrow.

    The photograph is an eighth of the actual size.

    Calculate the values of w and h.

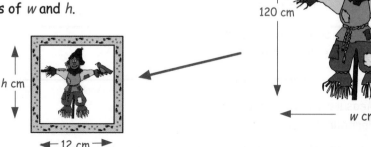

    120 cm

    h cm

    12 cm

    w cm

REVIEW 9

Ratio

1. In a butcher's shop window there are 103 mince pies, 79 curry pies and 58 steak pies.

   Write down the ratio of : -

   a   curry pies : mince pies
   b   steak pies : curry pies
   c   mince pies : steak pies
   d   curry pies : total number of pies.

2. Write down each ratio in its simplest form : -

   a   pentagons : hexagons
   b   squares : pentagons
   c   squares : rectangles
   d   quadrilaterals : hexagons
   e   quadrilaterals : other shapes

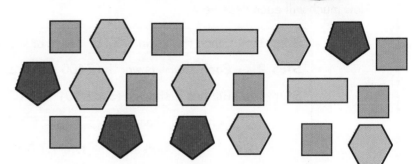

3. Write each of these ratios in its simplest form :-

   a   1 centimetre : 1 metre
   b   1 second : 1 minute
   c   10 minutes : 1 hour
   d   30p : £6
   e   1 day : 1 year
   f   50 centimetres : 2 metres
   g   £2·50 : £10
   h   days in February 2012 : days in June 2012.

4. In a week Rhona earns £450, Mary earns £500 and Vicky earns £650.

   Write down each of the following ratios of wages in their simplest form : -

   a   Rhona : Vicky
   b   Mary : total wages
   c   Vicky : Mary : Rhona.

5.  In Seaworld Centre, the ratio of sharks to seals is 3 : 5.

   a   If there are 27 sharks, how many seals must there be ?
   b   If there are 40 seals, how many sharks are there ?

6. Melanie is making a model ship to a scale of 1 : 50.

   a   Her model is 30 cm in height. What is the height of the real ship, in metres ?
   b   The real ship is 25 metres long. What length, in cm, should her model be ?

7.

   a   Share 27 rollos between Brain and Helen in the ratio of 2 : 1 so that Brian gets the larger share.

   b   If the rollos are shared in the ratio 5 : 4 with Brian still getting the larger share, how many more rollos will Helen get than in part a ?

CHAPTER 10

Proportion

Proportional Division

Be able to share in any given ratio

Sharing in a given ratio

Example :-

Bill and Ben share a prize of £400 in a ratio of 3 : 5.

How much will each receive ?

> **Step 1 :-** Since the ratio is 3 : 5, there are (3 + 5) = 8 shares
>
> **Step 2 :-** Each share is worth (£400 ÷ 8) = £50
>
> **Step 3 :-** Bill has 3 shares (3 × £50) = £150
>
> Ben has 5 shares (5 × £50) = £250
>
> (Check that the total for Ben and Bill is £400).

Exercise 1

1. Share £2000 between Sal and Seth in the ratio 2 : 3.

   Copy and complete : -

   > Total number of shares = 2 + 3 = <u>5</u>
   >
   > Each share = £2000 ÷ <u>5</u> = £400
   >
   > Sal has 2 shares = 2 × £..... = £......
   >
   > Seth has 3 shares = 3 × £..... = £......

   (check total is £2000).

2. Share £36 000 between James and Pauline in the ratio 2 : 7.
   (*Show all your working and remember to check your total comes to £36 000*).

3. Show all your working for each of the following :-

   a Share £45 000 between Peter and Paul in the ratio 4 : 11.

   b Share £12 000 between Anne and Tom in the ratio 7 : 5.

   c Share £8·60 between Gary and Dennis in the ratio 1 : 3.

   d Share €7140 between Pieter and Helena in the ratio 4 : 3.

   e Share one million pounds between Addy and Steve in the ratio 13 : 7.

4.

   Each week Ed and Edie share a £16 lottery ticket cost.
   Ed pays £12 and Edie pays £4.

   a Write the ratio of how much they pay in simplest form.

   b Last week their ticket won £2400.

   How much money should each receive ?

5. Beth (age 12) and Joshua (age 8) are left £100 000 in their Gran's will.
    The money is to be shared between Beth and Joshua **in the ratio of their ages**.

    How much should Joshua receive from his Gran's will ?

6.  Sam and Simon are in the final of a hot-dog eating contest.
    They will share the £600 prize money in the ratio of how
    many hot-dogs they each eat !
    Sam eats 14 hot-dogs. Simon eats 16 hot-dogs.

    How much **more** prize money did the winner receive than the runner-up ?

7. a   Share £600 amongst Al, Bo and Cal in the ratio 1 : 2 : 3

    b   Share £1000 amongst Addison, Bronte and Cairn in the ratio 1 : 3 : 6.

    c   Share $600 amongst Tam, Sam and Pam in the ratio 4 : 5 : 11.

8. A **Fifty kilometre** triathlon is to be held tomorrow.

    Each contestant will run, then swim and then cycle distances
    that are in the ratio 2 : 1 : 7.

    How far will each contestant :-

    a   run   b   swim   c   cycle ?

9. The new Up's & Downs Theatre show has a 2 hour running time.

    It is split into 3 timed sections in a ratio of 5 : 2 : 3.

    Write down the times of each section, in minutes.

10.  A fruit stall is set up in Market Square.
    The ratio of apples : oranges : pears is 5 : 8 : 2.
    There are 64 oranges.

    How many pieces of fruit are there ?

11. A drinks dispenser is programmed to give 35 litres of orange
    juice to three children each week in the ratio of their weights.

        Sebastian is half Henry's weight.
        Timmy is half Sebastian's weight.
        Henry weighs 40 kilograms.

    How much orange juice will each child be given in a week ?

12.  Two litres of Summer Punch are poured into three different punch bowls.

    The first bowl holds 200 ml.

    The 2nd bowl hold four times as much as the 1st bowl.

    Find the ratio of punch per bowl for the 3 bowls.

Proportion

Be able to use basic proportion to find the value of one item

If you know the total cost of several items,
you can easily find the cost per item.

Example :-   The cost of 5 pies is £4·00.

The cost of 1 pie = (£4·00 ÷ 5) = £0·80 – (simply divide).

Exercise 2   *Oral Exercise*

1.   The cost of 6 cakes is £6·30. Find the cost of one cake.

2.   Find the cost per item : -

    a   5 sweets costing 35p   b   9 shirts costing £108

    c   7 DVD's costing £63   d   11 ice-creams costing £2·20

    e   12 carrots costing £2·40   f   10 rabbits costing £210.

3.   It took a truck 60 trips to move 1200 tonnes of rubble.

How many tonnes did the truck move each trip ?

4.      A soldier can march 36 kilometres in 6 hours.

Calculate the rate in kilometres per hour.

5.   Jill exchanges £40 for 44 euros. What is the rate of € per £.

6.      A 4 kilogram bag of carrots costs £2.

What is the weight per £ ?

7.   A hamster rotates a running wheel 90 times in a minute.

Calculate the number of rotations per second.

8.   Jack was "Walking Round Scotland" for charity.

During the month of June, he travelled a total
distance of 480 miles.

How many miles (on average) did he travel each day ?

9.   David bought a set of 4 new tyres from Slow-Fit for a total of £96.
Tim bought a set of 5 similar tyres from Tyres 'R Us for £110.

Who got the better deal ?

Direct Proportion

Two quantities, (for example, the number of cakes and the total cost), are said to be in **direct proportion**, if : -

> "... when you double (treble, quadruple, half) the number of one item you double (treble, quadruple, half) the number of the other".

Example :- The cost of 6 cakes is £4·20. Find the cost of 5 cakes.

Set down
like this : -

Cakes		Cost
6	—>	4·20
1	—>	4·20 ÷ 6 = 0·70
5	—>	5 × 0·70 = £3·50

5 cakes cost £3·50

Exercise 3

1. The cost of 7 books is £65·80.

    Find the cost of 6 books.

Books		Cost
7	—>	£65·80
1	—>	£65·80 ÷ 7 = £......
6	—>	

2. Nine sheets of high gloss photo paper costs £7·29 How much would it cost for 10 sheets ?
    (*Find the cost of 1 sheet first*).

3. On holiday, Bronte exchanged £80 for $120.

    How many dollars would Bronte have got for £45 ?
    (*Find how much for £1 first*).

4. a   It takes a cement mixer 2 minutes to mix 1·2 cubic metres of cement.

        What volume of cement could the mixer do in 9 minutes ?

    b   A wheel turns 500 times in 4 minutes.

        How many turns would it make in 5 minutes ?

5. a   5 air-mail letters cost £4 to post.

        How much would it cost to post 6 letters ?

    b   Nine cakes cost £18·36. How much would ten cakes cost ?

TeeJay Publishers
PO Box 1365
Barrhead
Glasgow
G78 1JJ

6.

    A machine makes 3000 staples every 6 seconds.

    How many staples will it make in : -

    a   1 second   b   7 seconds

    c   one minute   d   an hour ?

7. Which of the following are examples of **direct proportion** ?

   a   5 cakes cost £3. Six cakes cost £3·50.   b   9 sweets cost 72p. Ten cost 81p.

   c   3 DVD's cost £42. Four DVD's cost £52.   d   11 pies cost £11·99. 5 pies cost £5·45.

8.    A bricklayer can lay 35 bricks in seven minutes.

   a   How many bricks could he lay in an hour ?

   b   How long would it take to build a wall with 250 bricks ?

9. A computer programmer writes 30 lines of computer code in an hour.

   a   How long would it take to write 25 lines of code ?

   b   It took 1 hour and 48 minutes to write a computer programme.

   How many lines of code were in this programme ?

Sometimes it is easier to find the cost of 10, or 100, or 1000 items first, instead of just 1 !

Example : -   500 coloured crayons cost £20. How much would it cost for 700 crayons ?

   This time it would be easier to find the cost of 100 first, then multiply by 7.

Crayons		Cost
500	—>	£20
100	—>	£20 ÷ 5 = £4
700	—>	£4 x 7 = £28

---

10. a   200 litres of olive oil costs £30. Find the cost of 150 litres.

    b   100 tyres take 5 hours to burn, one at a time. How long would it take 70 tyres to burn ?

    c   It takes 500 bees a week to make 3·5 kg of honey.

    What weight of honey would you get in a week from 400 bees ?

    d   600 ml of strawberry concentrate costs £2·40.

    How much would it cost for one litre ?

    e   60 metres of rope costs £24. How much would it cost for 24 metres ?

11.    The cost of painting is directly proportional to the area being painted.

    a   A corridor panel 12 metres by 3 metres costs £72 to paint.

    How much would it cost for a panel 15 metres by 3 metres ?

    b   A factory wall (25 metres by 8 metres) costs £160 to paint.

    How much would it cost to paint a 30 metres by 5 metres wall ?

Linear Graph of Direct Proportion

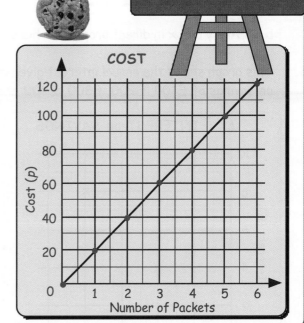

Be able to show direct proportion as a Linear Graph

The table below shows the cost of packets of "Biscuits".

No. of Pkts	1	2	3	4	5	6
Cost (p)	20	40	60	80	100	120

We can represent each pair as a set of coordinates.

(1, 20), (2, 40), (3, 60), (4, 80), etc...

Can you see that all of the points lie on a straight line, passing through the origin ?

This is true for any two quantities which are in DIRECT PROPORTION.

Exercise 4

1. a Copy and complete the table.

    b Using the same scales as in the above graph, plot the points (1, 30), (2, ?), ...

No. of Pears	1	2	3	4	5	6
Cost (p)	30	60				

    c (i) Join the points with a straight line

       (ii) Does the line pass through the origin ?

       (iii) Explain why the line must pass through the origin.

2. a Copy and complete this table.

    b Use an appropriate scale to plot the points (1, 40), (2, ...), etc.

No. of Pots	1	2	3	4	5	6
Cost (p)	40	80				

    c (i) Join the points with a straight line.

       (ii) Does the line pass through the origin ?

3. a Copy and complete this table for a cycle travelling at 15 km/hr.

    b Using a scale of 2 boxes to represent 1 hour on the horizontal axis and 2 boxes to represent 10 km on the vertical axis, plot the points and draw a line through them.

Time (hrs)	1	2	3	4	5	6
Distance (km)	15	30				

    c What distance should the cycle travel in :-   (i) 8 hours   (ii) $6\frac{1}{2}$ hrs ?

4. a   Draw a set of axes and plot the following points.

x	1	2	3	4
y	3	6	8	12

=> (1, 3), ..., etc.

A simple check for direct proportion is found by dividing each pair of values.

(3 ÷ 1), (6 ÷ 2), (8 ÷ 3), (12 ÷ 4)

If you always obtain the same value, then they are in direct proportion.

If even one of the values differs from the rest, they are **not** in direct proportion.

    b   Are *y* and *x* in direct proportion here ? *Explain.*

5. This graph shows the annual interest given by the "Scottish Building Society" on savings of £100, £200, £300, £400 and £500.

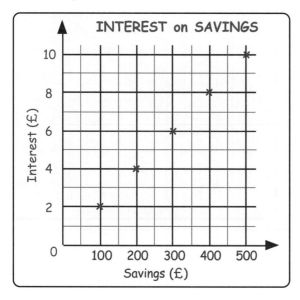

a   Use the graph to copy and complete this table.

Savings (£)	100	200	300	400	500	600
Interest (%)	2	4				

b   Are the quantities in direct proportion ? *Explain.*

c   Calculate the interest gained on savings of £1000 ?

6. Which two of the following tables indicate examples of direct proportion ? (*hint - divide*)

a
x	1	2	3	4
y	1	4	9	16

b
x	1	2	3	4
y	5	10	20	40

c
w	1	2	3	4
P	2	4	6	8

d
m	1	2	3	4
S	5	4	3	2

e
d	1	2	3	4
H	0	2	6	10

f
z	1	2	3	4
T	30	60	90	120

7. For each of your two answers to question 6, verify they are in direct proportion by plotting the points and showing a line can be drawn through these points and the origin.

8. Work in pairs or groups - the best graphs may be used on the wall of your classroom.

    a   Find a currency exchange rate used somewhere in the world.

    b   On graph paper write a report using a direct proportion graph and explain why such a graph could be used for currency conversion.

    c   Discuss other places where direct proportion is used.

1. a One shirt costs £7. How much would it cost for 4 shirts ?

   b One pair of boots costs £45. How much would it be for 3 pairs ?

   c Six vests are needed for football training.

   How much will it cost in total if one costs £3·25 ?

2. a Five melons cost £5·25.

   How much would it be for one melon ?

   b Ten boxes of strawberries costs £17·50.

   How much would it cost for each box ?

3. a Three ties cost £18. How much would two ties cost ?

   b Seven bars of soap costs £14·70. How much would three bars cost ?

   c How much would five chairs cost, if four chairs cost £56 ?

4.  These three toy cars cost £18·99.

   How much would four cars cost ?

5. a Which is the better deal when buying pies ?

   b Explain why.

   Tray of 10 pies – £12·20

   Tray of 8 pies – £9·60

6. a Share £6000 in a ratio of 2 : 1.   b Share 180 grapes in a 2 : 3 ratio.

7. Sara, Tina and Una won a million pounds in the lottery.
   Their winnings are to be split into a 5 : 3 : 2 ratio.

   How much will each girl receive ?

8. a Copy and complete this table for a van travelling at 50 km/hr.

   b Using a scale of 2 boxes to represent 1 hour on the horizontal axis and 2 boxes to represent 10 km on the vertical axis, plot the points and draw a line through them.

Time (hrs)	1	2	3	4	5	6
Distance (km)	50	100				

   c How far will the van travel in 9 hours ?

REVIEW 10 ✓

Percentages, Fractions & Decimals

1. Change each of the following into decimals and fractions in their **simplest form** :-

     a   37%   b   80%   c   75%   d   2·5%.

2. Change each fraction into a decimal (to three decimal places) and then to a percentage :-

     a $\frac{1}{8}$ b $\frac{8}{11}$ c $\frac{17}{70}$ d $\frac{432}{777}$.

3. Write the following list in order, **smallest first** :-

     47%,   0·46, $\frac{1}{2}$, $\frac{147}{300}$,   0·05.

4. Jake scored the following in 3 tests :-

     English $^{56}/_{70}$ Physics $^{42}/_{60}$ Music $^{15}/_{20}$.

     Which was his best score ? *Explain*.

5. Calculate :-

     a   24% of 120 kg   b   15% of 80 m   c   55% of 10 km   d   17·5% of £1240

     e   70% of £1   f   11% of 5 cm   g   48% of 680 ml   h   3·2% of £6200.

6. At a local derby 76% of the 8600 crowd were home supporters.

     a   What was the percentage of the away supporters ?

     b   How many away supporters were at the match ?

7.   a   There is a 30% discount on a pair of football boots costing £45.

        How much do the football boots cost in the sale ?

   b   A football strip costing £68 is to have its price increased by 15%.

        How much will the strip now cost ?

8.   a   A town raised £8000 last year to save their local church.
        This year they need to raise 20% more than last year.

        How much do they need to raise this year ?

   b   A congregation of 1800 attended a church in 2010.
        The attendance in 2011 rose by 10%.
        The 2012 attendance dropped by 10% from the previous year's figure.

        What was the attendance in 2012 ?

CHAPTER 11

Line Symmetry   *Revision*

Be able to identify line symmetry and create symmetrical shapes

Remember :-   A line of symmetry occurs in a shape if, when the shape is folded over the line, "*the two pieces, either side of the line, are exactly the same*".

These shapes have lines of symmetry :-

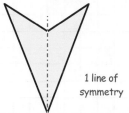

1 line of symmetry

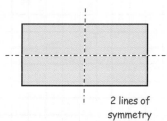

2 lines of symmetry

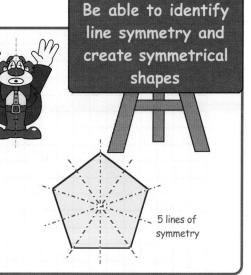

5 lines of symmetry

Exercise 1

1. Make a neat tracing of each of the following shapes.

    Use a coloured pencil to show all the lines of symmetry.

    Write down beside each shape how many lines of symmetry it has.

a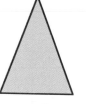

b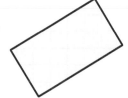

c

d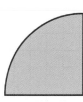

e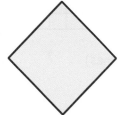

f

g

h

i

j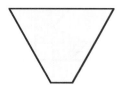

k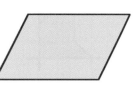

l

m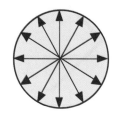

n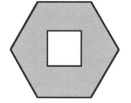

o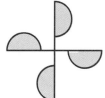

p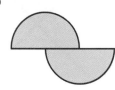

2. Copy each of the following shapes neatly and complete each one such that the **red dotted** line is a line of symmetry each time.

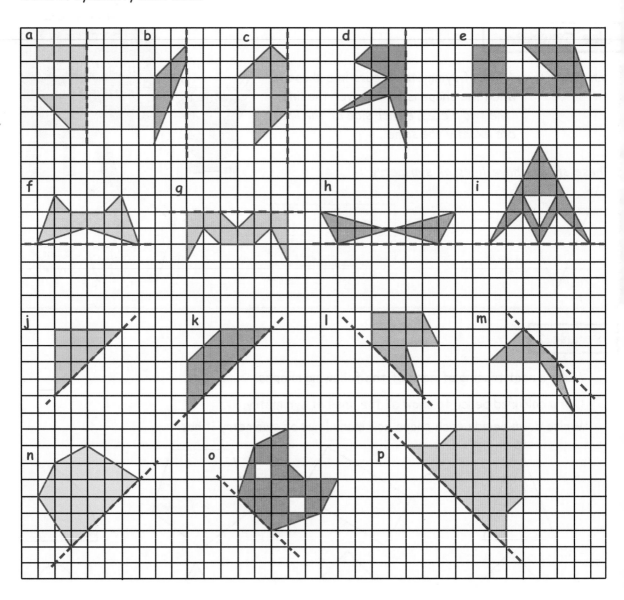

3. This time, each shape has to have 2 lines of symmetry (shown as **red lines**) Carefully copy and complete each shape.

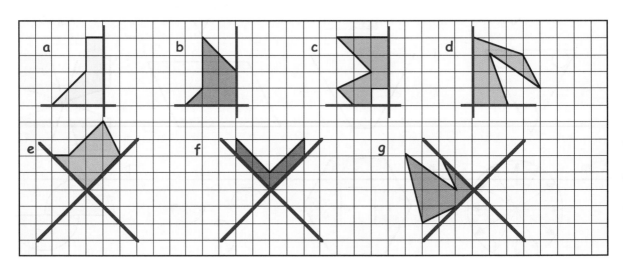

Look at the shape opposite.

Can you see that it has
NO lines of symmetry ?

Can you also see that if you
"spin" the shape by 180°
(half a turn) around the red dot, it
will fit back onto its own outline ?

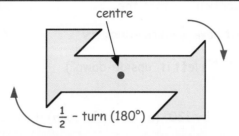

centre

$\frac{1}{2}$ – turn (180°)

We say :-   It has "$\frac{1}{2}$ – turn symmetry".   (or Rotational Symmetry "of order 2").

Exercise 2

1.   Which of the following shapes have half-turn symmetry ?

a 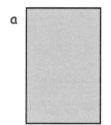   b 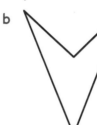   c 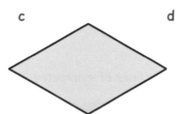   d

e 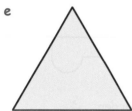   f 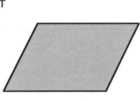   g 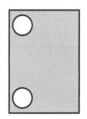   h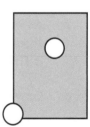

i 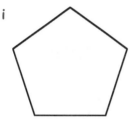   j 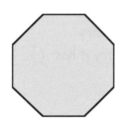   k 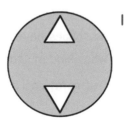   l

m    n    o 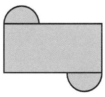   p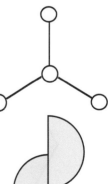

q 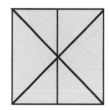   r 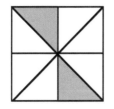   s 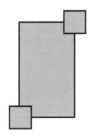   t

Turn Symmetry (continued).

You should have found in question 1 e that the

equilateral triangle does not have $\frac{1}{2}$ –turn symmetry

(Rotating it by a half turn (180°) left it "upside-down").

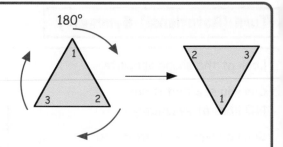

However, if you rotate it by 120° (a **third** of a turn) it will fit back onto itself.

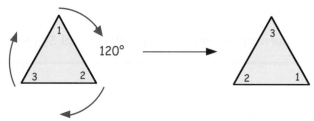

we say :-   It has "$\frac{1}{3}$ –turn symmetry".   (or Rotational Symmetry "of order 3").

2.   Look at this shape

   a   Does it have any lines of symmetry ?

   It obviously has "half-turn symmetry".

   b   As well as 180°, what **smaller** angle could the
        shape be rotated by around its centre so that
        it fitted back onto itself ?
                                        insert a fraction

   c   Copy and complete :-

        "The shape has ..... - turn symmetry, or rotational symmetry of order ...".

3.   Some of the following shapes have "**turn symmetry**".
      For each shape, say what kind of "turn" symmetry it has. ($\frac{1}{2}$, $\frac{1}{3}$, $\frac{1}{4}$, $\frac{1}{5}$, $\frac{1}{6}$, $\frac{1}{8}$, etc),
      and state the "order" of rotational symmetry.

   a   b    c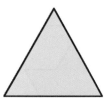

   d 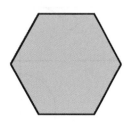   e 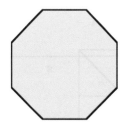   f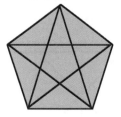

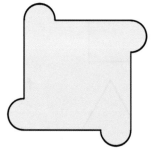

3.

g   h   i

j   k   l

m   n   o

p   q   r

s   t   u

v   w   x

4. Draw some shapes of your own to show turn symmetry of :- $\frac{1}{2}$, $\frac{1}{3}$, $\frac{1}{4}$, $\frac{1}{5}$, $\frac{1}{6}$, $\frac{1}{8}$,.....

Creating a Shape with Half-Turn Symmetry

Be able to create a shape using turn symmetry

If we take a given shape and spin it 180° around a fixed point, then this new shape, along with the original will form a figure which will have $\frac{1}{2}$ - turn symmetry.

In this diagram, the dot has to be the centre of symmetry .

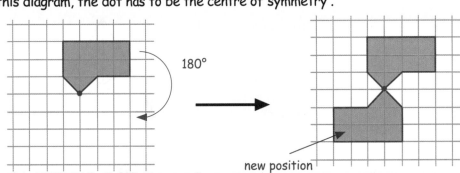

180°

new position

Exercise 3

1. a   Make a copy of this rectangle.

    b   Now rotate it by a $\frac{1}{2}$ turn around the red dot.

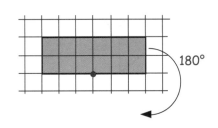

2.   Copy this figure and rotate it by half a turn around the red dot.

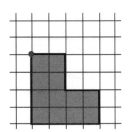

3.   Do the same here with this triangular shape.

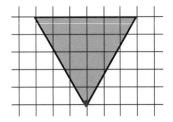

4.   Make a copy of each of the following shapes neatly and carefully.
     Create a shape which has got half turn symmetry by rotating each shape by 180° around the red dot :-

a

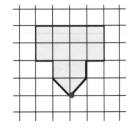

b

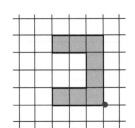

c

4. d 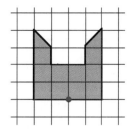   e 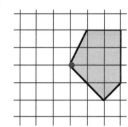   f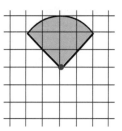

g 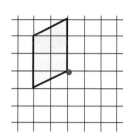   h 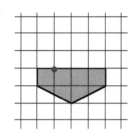   i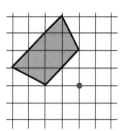

j 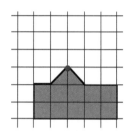   k 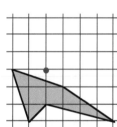   l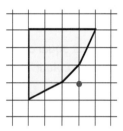

m 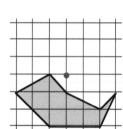   n 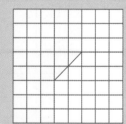   o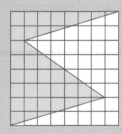

5. Look at the three 8 by 8 squares.

Each has a continuous unbroken line drawn through them dividing the shape into 2 parts in such a way that the shape has half turn symmetry.

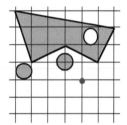

a   Draw the 8 x 8 square several times and try to find imaginative ways of dividing the shape with <u>one</u> continuous unbroken line such that the shape has half turn symmetry around its centre.

b   Use two colours to shade each half in and make a display of the best.

c   Try to create some of your own complicated diagrams similar to the diagrams above that show half turn symmetry.

Shown is a 3 by 2 rectangular tile.

It is easy to see that if you have lots of tiles congruent* to this one, you can cover an area using them, with NO gaps.

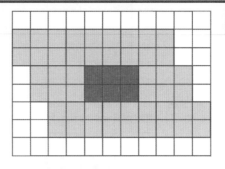

In Mathematics terms, we say :-

"The rectangle tiles the surface". (or tiles the "plane").

*congruent - two shapes are congruent if they are exactly the same size and shape.

Exercise 4

1. a Copy this square (3 by 3) tile onto squared paper. Shade or colour it in as the starter tile.

   b Completely surround it with congruent tiles to show that the square will "tile the plane".

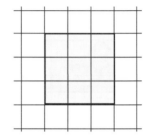

2.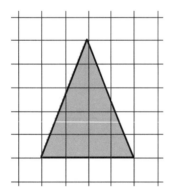

   a Copy this triangular tile onto squared paper and shade or colour it in.

   b Completely surround it with congruent tiles to show that the triangle will "tile the plane".

   (Note :- even if you turn a tile upside down it will still be congruent to the original).

3. a Make a copy of this rhombic tile.

   b Completely surround it with congruent tiles to show that the rhombus will "tile the plane".

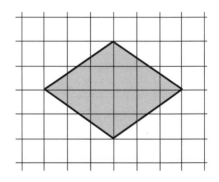

4.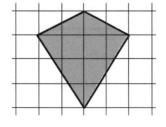

   a Copy this kite-shaped tile onto squared paper and shade or colour it in.

   b Completely surround it with congruent tiles to show that the kite will "tile the plane".

5. Shown below are various shapes.

   Without actually drawing them, decide which shapes are most likely to "tile the plane".

   a  b  c 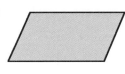 d

   e 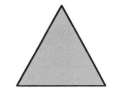 f 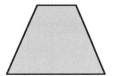 g   h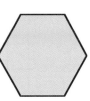

   i 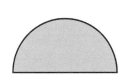 j  k  l

   m 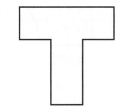 n 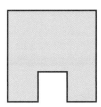 o 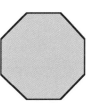 p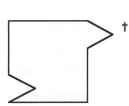

   q 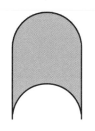 r 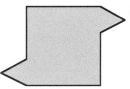 s 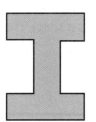 t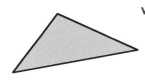

   u 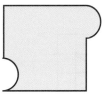 v  w

6. This shape is called a V-kite.

   a   Copy it carefully and shade it in.

   b   Show, by surrounding it with congruent shapes, that the V-kite tiles the plane.

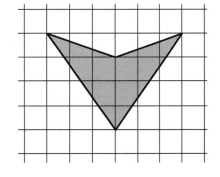

7. Do the same for each of the following.

   (i) Draw each shape and shade it in.

   (ii) Surround each shape completely with a set of congruent tiles.

   a 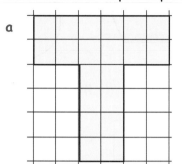   b 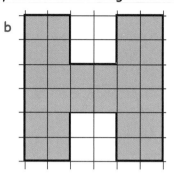   c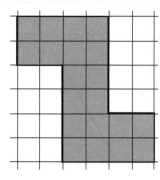

8. This one is a bit trickier.

   Draw the tile carefully, shade it in and
   surround it with a set of congruent tiles.

   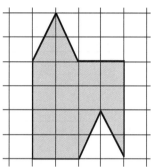

9. Here is how to create your own **FUN** tile :-

   Step 1 Start with a simple shape that does tile,
   like a square or rectangle.

   Step 2 Draw it onto cardboard.

   Step 3 Cut a simple shape (like a triangle)
   out from the bottom corner.

   Step 4 Sellotape the triangle on the top corner
   in the corresponding position.

   Step 5 This now gives a shape that tiles.

   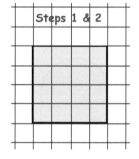

   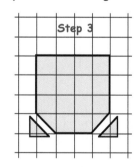   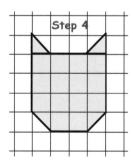   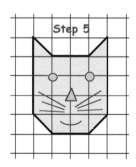

   Use your piece of card as a template to draw a pattern of "cat faces".

10. Design your own template. Start with a simple shape like a square, rectangle or
    equilateral triangle. Draw it on card and cut it out.

    Use your template to create a repetitive pattern.

Revisit - Review - Revise

1. Write down how many lines of symmetry are in each of these shapes :-

a 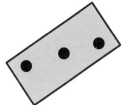   b    c

d 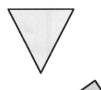   e 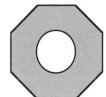   f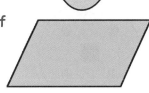

2. Copy these four shapes neatly on to squared paper and complete the diagrams so that the red lines are lines of symmetry :-

a 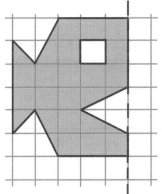   b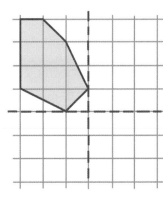

c 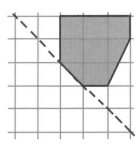   d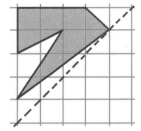

3. Which, if any, of these shapes have half turn symmetry ?

a 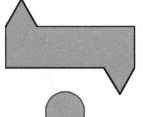   b 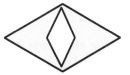   c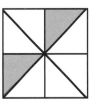

d    e   f

4. Each of the following shapes has rotational symmetry.

Say what kind of turn symmetry, ($\frac{1}{2}$, $\frac{1}{3}$, ...), and state the **order** of rotational symmetry.

a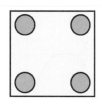

b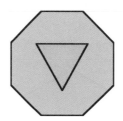

c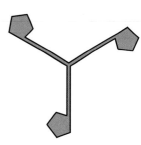

d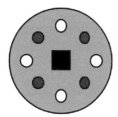

e

f

5. Copy these two shapes and give each of them a half turn around the dot.

a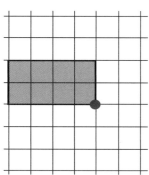

b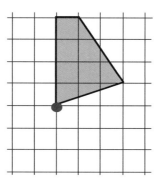

6.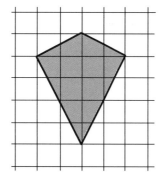

a Make a copy of this kite-shaped tile in the **centre of a page in your jotter** and shade it.

b Show how to completely surround it with congruent tiles.

7. Which of the following shapes will tile the plane ?

a

b

c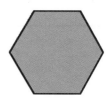

d

REVIEW 11

 ✓

The Circle

. For a circle, write down the formula for finding its :- a circumference b area.

. a Use the correct formula to calculate the **circumferences** of these circles :-
(answers to 3 significant figures)

(i)
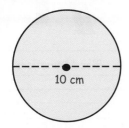
10 cm

(ii)

Diameter
2·8 cm

(iii)

4 cm

b Now use the correct formula to calculate the **areas** of the circles.

. A boy flies a model plane in a circle around his head.

The radius of its circular path is 50 centimetres.

Work out the length of the path of the plane.

50 cm

. Four semi-circular rods are used to form the top
of a fence 160 centimetres long.

a Calculate the length of one of the semi-circular rods.

b Calculate the length of all 4 rods, plus their bases.

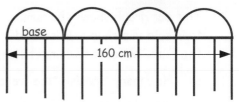
base
160 cm

.  The circumference of this baked potato is 37·68 cm.

Use an appropriate formula to work out its **radius**.

. Calculate the **perimeter** and the **area** of each of these shapes :-

a
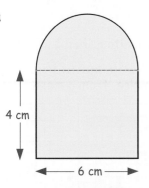
4 cm
6 cm

b
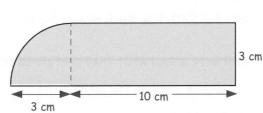
3 cm
3 cm
10 cm

c
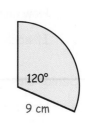
120°
9 cm

.
3 m
6 m
6 m

A large square area of paving with side 6 metres had a quarter
circle with radius 3 m cut from it so that a flower bed could be
laid.

Calculate the area of the paving which remained.

CHAPTER 12

Bar Graphs and Line Graphs

Remember how to interpret and draw a bar graph & a line graph

Exercise 1   *Mainly Revision*

1. Write down a list of things that a bar graph must always have.

2. The bar graph shows the number of people who donated blood in the transfusion van one week last winter.

    a   How many people gave blood on :-

    (i)   Monday   (ii)   Tuesday

    (iii)   Friday   (iv)   Thursday ?

    b   How many people gave blood in total that week ?

    c   The transfusion van's heating system broke down one day and the staff were sent home.

    Which day was that ? Give a reason for your answer.

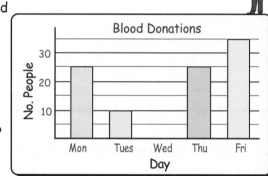

3. This bar graph shows the number of football tops sold in a shop in Gretna, during the Euro '12 football competition.

    a   How many Spanish tops were sold ?

    b   What was the least popular strip sold ?

    c   Which two strips sold the same quantity and how many of each was that ?

    d   State an obvious reason for the high sales of English tops in this sports shop ?

    e   How many more England than Germany tops were sold ?

    f   If each top was sold for £40, how much money did the shop take in altogether ?

4. Senior classes in a school were asked what they preferred to eat with rice, from a menu.

    a   How many shell fish dishes were on the menu ?

    b   How many Seniors preferred :-

    (i)   Chilli Beef   (ii)   Prawns

    (iii)   Pork   (iv)   Chicken ?

    c   What was the most liked food with rice ?

    d   How many more seniors chose prawns than pork ?

    e   How many less chose stir fry than chicken ?

    f   How many were asked altogether ?

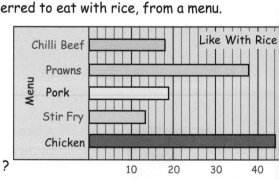

this bar graph is called a **Horizontal Bar Graph**

5. The owner of a small shop asked her 30 loyal customers what kind of tinned soup they liked.

   The results are shown in the table :-

pea/ham	tomato	chicken	lentil	oxtail	minestrone
3	9	4	7	1	6

   Draw and label a neat **bar graph** to show this information.

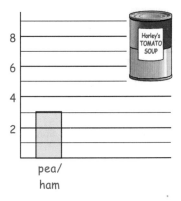

6. Kerry's Electrical Store carried out a survey into which TV channel their customers preferred to view. Here are the results of that survey :-

ITV 1	BBC 1	Ch 4	Ch 5	Sky 1	Sky Sports	Sky Movies
45	30	10	25	50	60	5

   Decide on a **suitable scale** and draw/label a neat **bar graph** to illustrate these findings.

7. A patient's temperature was taken every hour from 6 am until 1 pm.

   The results are shown in this line graph.

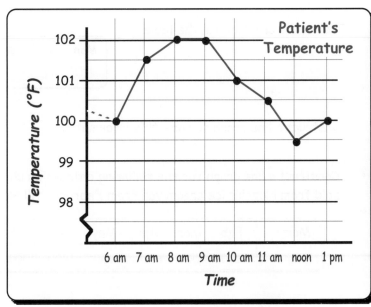

   a   When was the patient's temperature at its lowest ?

   b   When was it at its highest ?

   c   By how many degrees did it rise between 6 am and 8 am ?

   d   At which two times did the temperature begin to rise ?

   e   At 9 am, his temperature began to fall.
       For how long did this last and by how many degrees did it fall ?

   f   What was his estimated temperature at 11.30 am ?

8. Two tent companies .....

   • The Tent Store (in red) and

   • Tents-for-U (in green)

   compare their sales.

   The **comparative line graph** gives
   the sales in hundreds of units.

   a   State the sales of The Tent Store in :-

        (i)   April   (ii)   July   (iii)   October.

   b   State the sales of Tents-for-U in :-

        (i)   March   (ii)   June   (iii)   September.

   c   Whose sales were lower in :-

        (i)   May   (ii)   August   (iii)   November ?

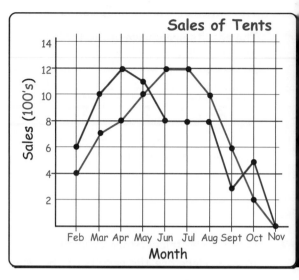

   The Tent Store made a £30 profit on each tent.

   Tents-for-U made a £25 profit on each tent.

   d   (i)   Who made **more** profit in May ?

        (ii)   How much **more** did that company make in May ?

9. The temperature in a classroom (°C) was recorded every day at noon for a week.

   The results are shown in the table :-

Mon	Tue	Wed	Thu	Fri
10	8	9	10·5	4·5

   Construct a line graph to show this information.

10. Construct a line graph for the following data which shows the number of ice creams
    sold from Napoli's ice cream van from February till November 2012.

Month	Feb	Mar	Apr	May	Jun	Jul	Aug	Sep	Oct	Nov
Sales	100	200	600	1000	1200	1000	900	500	100	50

   Make your vertical scale go up in 200's.

11. This table shows 6 months of car sales from
    two different car dealers, Arnold Clunk
    and Reg Barney.

    Construct a **comparative line graph**
    to show this information.

	Jul	Aug	Sep	Oct	Nov	Dec
Clunk's	100	250	300	250	400	200
Barney's	300	200	350	450	100	150

Spreadsheets and Databases

Access to a computer would help with this topic, but tables could be drawn up and completed manually.

Be able to understand spreadsheets & databases

A **spreadsheet** is simply a computerised table of values that can be used to do calculations on these values or **entries**.

The boxes in the table are called **cells**.

This is cell D3.

	A	B	C	D	E
1					
2					
3					
4					
5					

Example :-

A group of 4 First Year pupils are comparing their marks in three of their maths tests.

David Smith scored   62%, 81% and 79%.   Brian Jones scored   63%, 59% and 91%.

Bobby Young scored   71%, 83% and 65%   Allan Taylor scored   73%, 76% and 79%.

Cell A1 is used for the 1st name and **cell B1** is used for the 2nd name, etc.

The first 3 lines of the table would look like this :-

	A	B	C	D	E
1	First	Second	Test 1	Test 2	Test 3
2					
3	David	Smith	62	81	79

Exercise 2

1. a   Open up a new spreadsheet or draw up a spreadsheet table and fill in the relevant cells to show the test marks for all 4 boys.

   b   Keep your table for later or print out and **save** your spreadsheet for later. (*Spreadsheet 1*).

2. A glazier is cutting a series of rectangular panes of glass for six customers.
   He is going to calculate the area and cost of each piece eventually.

   a   Open a new spreadsheet or draw up a table with the headings :

   cell A1 – Customer   cell B1 – length (cm)   cell C1 – breadth (cm)

   b   Fill in the following customer details, starting in cell A3:

   Mr Davies - 60 cm by 80 cm   Mrs White - 90 cm by 120 cm

   Mr Gordon - 210 cm by 160 cm   Mrs Wylie - 75 cm by 160 cm

   Mr Rivers   - 130 cm by 110 cm   Mrs Jones - 80 cm by 150 cm.

   c   Your spreadsheet should look like this.

   d   Save this for later.

   e   Take a printout of your spreadsheet and save it. (*Spreadsheet 2*).

	A	B	C
1	Customer	Length (cm)	breadth (cm)
2			
3	Mr Davies	60	....

Calculations in Spreadsheets

Be able to use a spreadsheet to do calculations

A spreadsheet is particularly useful for doing multiple calculations.

Example :-

Look back at your *Spreadsheet 1* and imagine we wish to find each boy's **average**.

	A	B	C	D	E	F
1	First	Second	Test 1	Test 2	Test 3	Average
2						
3	David	Smith	62	81	79	

Add on a 6th column to your table and type in **Average** in cell F1.

Now we can get the computer to calculate the average of David's 3 test results as follows :-

· In cell **F3**, type in "=(C3 + D3 + E3)/3" and press **return**. When you do this, **74** should appear.

· Click on cell **F3**, copy it and paste it into cell **F4**. Cell F4 should now be **71** for Brian.

· Repeat the copying and pasting into cells **F5** and **F6** to complete the table.

Exercise 3

1. a Complete the above spreadsheet or fill in the 6th column of your table by doing the calculations manually.

   b Explain how a computer generated spreadsheet might save you time.
   (*Hint* :- Think about finding the average of a whole class or year group).

2. a In *Spreadsheet 2* (or Table 2), add a 4th column and in cell **D1**, type **AREA**.

   b In cell **D3**, type in the calculation needed to work out the **area** of Mr Davies' sheet of glass.
   (*Remember to begin your calculation with = and use cells B1 and C1*). Check it works.

   c Click on cell **D3**, copy it and paste it into cells **D4, D5, D6, D7,** and **D8** to complete the table.

3. A fruit shop computerises its pricing.

   a Open a new spreadsheet or table and enter the headings :
      cell A1 – fruit, cell B1 – weight (kg) and cell C1 – cost / kg

   b Fill in Mr Stevenson's fruit order, starting at cell A3.

      Mr Stevenson :-   2·5 kg of apples
                          1·5 kg of oranges
                          0·5 kg of grapes
                          3 kg of bananas
                          0 kg of pears
                          0·75 kg of peaches.

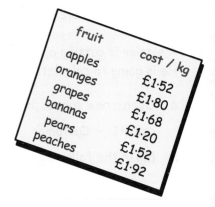

fruit	cost / kg
apples	£1·52
oranges	£1·80
grapes	£1·68
bananas	£1·20
pears	£1·52
peaches	£1·92

   c Add the heading COST in cell **D1**.

   d In cell **D3**, type = B3 * C3.

   e Copy and paste to complete the table.

   f In cell **D10**, type = D3 + D4 + D5 + D6 + D7 + D8 to obtain the total for the bill.

	A	B	C	D
1	fruit	weight kg	cost per kg	COST
2				
3	apples	2.5	£1.52	

4. Bloggs Engineers employs six workers. They wish to calculate the weekly wages of their workforce.

Name	Basic hours	Overtime hours*	Basic Rate of Pay*
Fred	40 hours	6 hours	£6·50 / hour.
Tom	38 hours	4 hours	£6·20 / hour.
Gina	36 hours	5 hours	£4·80 / hour.
Alex	39 hours	4 hours	£5·10 / hour.
Sara	40 hours	2 hours	£6·40 / hour.
Dave	32 hours	0 hours	£5·30 / hour.

* Overtime pay is at "time and a half" or 1·5 times basic pay.

a   Open a new spreadsheet or draw up a new table and enter these headings in the cells :-

cell A1 – Name, cell B1 – Rate of pay, cell C1 – Basic Hrs, cell D1 – Overtime Hrs.

b   Now enter the details for the 6 workers starting at cell A3.

c   Add on the following headings :- cell E1 - basic pay, cell F1 - O'time pay, cell G1 - Total pay,

d   Insert calculations in cells E3 and F3 find basic and overtime pays. Cell G3 = cell E3 + cell F3.

e   In cell G10, insert a calculation that will find the total wage bill for Bloggs Engineers.

5. a   Open up a new spreadsheet. In the spreadsheet, starting at cell C3, type in the 5 headings :-

Customer, Item 1, Item 2, Item 3, and Total.

b   Fill in the following three customers' details starting at cell C5 :-

Mr Jones   -   £3·85,   £9·62,   £4·75
Mrs Paton   -   £6·94,   £5·73,   £11·64
Mr Wilson   -   £9·85,   £7·24,   £1·68

c   Instead of entering = D5 + E5 + F5 into cell G5 to find the sum, try the following instead :-

Click on cell G5 and type in =SUM(click on cells D5, E5 and F5 in turn, close the bracket and press return. Did it work ?

d   Copy cell G5 and paste into cells G6 and G7.

e   Use a similar =SUM(....) to find the total of cells G5, G6 and G7, and paste into cell G9.

6. Go back and open the spreadsheet from Question 4.

a   Extend the spreadsheet to include two new headings in cells H1 and I1 :-

"Deductions" and "Net Pay".

b   In the appropriate cells, add in the 6 employees' details:

Employee	Fred	Tom	Gina	Alex	Sara	Dave
Deductions	£92·40	£75·30	£57·79	£52·72	£68·77	£31·42

c   Use a standard function, or devise your own to calculate Fred's net pay from his gross pay and his deductions, and copy your formula down to find the net pay of the other five.

7. Devise some spreadsheets of your own for questions involving topics such as profit and loss, hire purchase, bank interest, discounts, etc.

Interpreting and Drawing Pie Charts

Exercise 4   *Mainly Revision*

1.   The pie chart shows the results of a survey into favourite sandwiches bought from a snack bar.

Favourite Sandwich

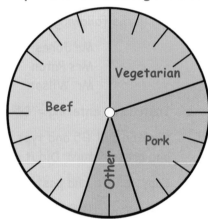

   a   Write down the fraction (/10) of people who chose :-

   (i)   Prawn   (ii)   Tuna

   (iii) Ham   (iv)   Chicken Mayo.

   b   List the sandwiches in order, from most popular to least popular.

   c   If 300 people were asked, how many of them liked :-

   (i)   Tuna   (ii)   Ham

   (iii) Prawn   (iv)   Chicken Mayo ?

2.   This pie chart, showing the sale of sausages in a supermarket one Saturday, has been divided into 20 equal parts.

Supermarket Sausage Sales

   a   What percentage does each part stand for ?

   b   What percentage represents :-

   (i)   Beef   (ii)   Pork

   (iii) Other   (iv)   Vegetarian ?

   4000 sausages were sold altogether that day.

   c   How many of the sausages sold were :-

   (i)   Pork   (ii)   Vegetarian

   (iii) Beef   (iv)   Other ?

3.   24 cooks were asked to name their favourite pie filling.

   a   What fraction of them voted for mince pie ? $\frac{90}{360}$ simplified

Favourite Pie Filling

   b   What fraction of them voted for :-

   (i)   Rhubarb   (ii)   Steak

   (iii) Cherry   (iv)   Apple ?

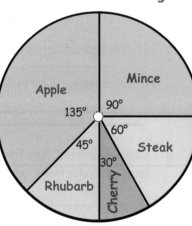

   c   Of the 24 cooks, how many voted for :-

   (i)   Mince   (ii)   Rhubarb

   (iii) Steak   (iv)   Cherry ?

   d   How many did that leave voting for apple pie ?

4. To make her home-made Macaroni Bake, Jenny
   uses only four ingredients as follows :-

   · 40% macaroni pasta

   · 30% tomato soup

   · 20% diced ham

   · 10% cheese

   Draw a pie chart to show this information.

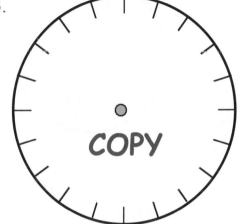

On a Mediterranean cruise, it was discovered that :-

· 35% of those on the ship were aged 20 - 65 years old

· 40% were senior citizens

· 20% were under 20 years old

   a   If the remainder on board were crew members
       what percentage was that ?

   b   Copy (or trace) the blank pie chart and complete
       it showing the above information.

6. The information given below shows the most popular answers to the question :-

   "If you were given money to renovate one room in your house,
   which room would you choose" ?

   ·   45% said "kitchen"

   ·   25% said "bathroom"

   ·   of the others, half said "bedroom"
       and half said "living room".

   Draw a pie chart to illustrate this, using a "pie" like this one.

7.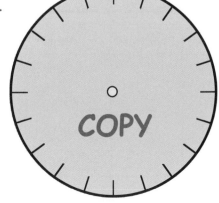

There were 60 000 people at Hampden Park, Glasgow.

· 30 000 were supporting Queens Park

· 15 000 were Alloa Athletic supporters

· 12 000 were neutral supporters

· the remainder were football officials and stewards.

   a   Copy (or trace) the blank pie chart and complete
       it to show the above information.

   b   What do you think is meant by "neutral" supporter ?

The table of data shows the number of different vehicles parked in a car/bus park.

When drawing a pie chart, it is sometimes easier to add columns to the table for calculations.

Type of Vehicle	Number
Car	36
Taxi	24
Bus	20
Motorcycle	10

Type of Vehicle	Number	Fraction	Angle
Car	36	$\frac{36}{90}$	$\frac{36}{90} \times 360 = 144°$
Taxi	24	$\frac{24}{90}$	$\frac{24}{90} \times 360 = 96°$
Bus	20	$\frac{20}{90}$	$\frac{20}{90} \times 360 = 80°$
Motorcycle	10	$\frac{10}{90}$	$\frac{10}{90} \times 360 = 40°$
TOTAL	90	1	360°

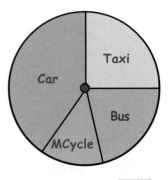

- **Step 1**   is to add up the Numbers column to get a total (in this case 90).

- **Step 2**   is to express each "Number" as a fraction of this total. (e.g. $\frac{36}{90}$).

- **Step 3**   is to find that fraction of 360° each time   (e.g. $\frac{36}{90} \times 360 = 144°$).

- **Step 4**   is finally to draw the pie chart using the angles in the table and a protractor.

Exercise 5

1. a   Copy and complete the table showing a group of 180 people's favourite vegetable.

    b   Construct a pie chart using a pair of compasses, a ruler and a protractor and the table information.

Vegetable	Number	Fraction	Angle
Lettuce	90	$\frac{90}{180}$	$\frac{90}{180} \times 360 = 180°$
Carrot	60	$\frac{60}{180}$	$\frac{60}{180} \times 360 = ...°$
Turnip	20	$\frac{}{180}$	$\frac{}{180} \times 360 = ...°$
Cabbage	10	$\frac{}{180}$	$\frac{}{180} \times 360 = ...°$
TOTAL	180	1	360°

2. a   Copy and complete this table which shows the number of grades a class obtained in their maths test.

    b   Construct an accurate pie chart showing this information.

Grades	Number	Fraction	Angle
A	3	$\frac{3}{45}$	$\frac{3}{45} \times 360 = 24°$
B	21	$\frac{21}{45}$	$\frac{21}{45} \times 360 = ...°$
C	17	$\frac{}{45}$	$\frac{}{45} \times 360 = ...°$
D	4	$\frac{}{45}$	$\frac{}{45} \times 360 = ...°$
TOTAL	45	1	360°

3. a Copy and complete the table showing motorists' favourite colour of car.

Car Colour	Number	Fraction	Angle
Red	7	$\frac{7}{30}$	$\frac{7}{30}$ x 360 = ...°
Silver	4		x 360 = ...°
Blue	6		x 360 = ...°
Black	13		x 360 = ...°
TOTAL	30		360°

b Construct an accurate pie chart showing this information.

4. For each table below, copy it (adding new columns to show your working) and construct an accurate pie chart to show the information.

a

Favourite TV Soap	Number
Corma Street	32
Westenders	24
Nummerdale	3
Next Door	13
TOTAL	....

b

Women's Ages	Number
60 - 64	380
65 - 69	260
70 - 74	60
75 - 79	20
TOTAL	....

5. The table shows the results of a survey asking people's favourite English holiday resort.

Torquay	Brighton	York	Blackpool	York	Blackpool	Brighton	Torquay
Blackpool	York	Brighton	Blackpool	Brighton	Blackpool	York	Blackpool
Brighton	Blackpool	Southport	Torquay	Brighton	Southport	Blackpool	Blackpool
York	Brighton	Southport	Blackpool	Blackpool	Torquay	Southport	York
Brighton	Blackpool	Blackpool	Blackpool	Brighton	Blackpool	Brighton	Torquay

a Copy and complete the table below :-

Hotel	Tally Mark	Number	Fraction	Angle
Blackpool				
Torquay				
York				
Brighton				
Southport				

b Using a pair of compasses, a ruler and a protractor, construct an accurate pie chart for this information.

Be able to calculate the range and the mean from a set of data

The Range is a mathematical tool used to measure how widely spread out a set of numbers are.

Range = Highest Score – Lowest Score

Example :-

The set of numbers 4, 2, 5, 7, 7, 12, 17, 8, 6, 9,

=> Range = 17 – 2 = 15.

The Mean (or average) of a set of scores is found by :-

· adding all the scores together

· then dividing by how many scores there are.

$$\text{Mean} = \frac{\text{Total of all the scores}}{\text{Number of scores}}$$

Example :-   Find the mean of :- 10, 8, 1 and 9.

$$\text{Mean} = \frac{10 + 8 + 1 + 9}{4} = \frac{28}{4} = 7$$

Exercise 6

1. Calculate the range and the mean of :-

   a   7, 12, 9, 4

   b   10, 27, 15, 19, 24

   c   £7, £6, £13, £27, £26, £5

   d   11 cm, 24 cm, 38 cm, 30 cm, 16 cm , 37 cm

   e   9·1, 7·2, 6·7, 9·6, 9·9, 6·8, 10·4, 4·3, 7·1

   f   4·87, 9·76, 8·93, 15·86, 4·58.

2. George spends his 4 month summer break from art school cleaning the floors and windows in his local gallery.

   For this, he gets paid a total of £1303·56.

   What does that **average** out at per month ?

3. Ten branches of Mason's Stores place bubble gum machines outside each shop.

   They find that they contain the following number of bubble gums :-

   50, 52, 54, 52, 55, 51, 53, 50, 54, 54.

   a   Work out the range.

   b   Calculate the mean number of bubble gums.

   c   The Bubble Gum Company claim that each of their machines should contain an average of 53 bubble gums.

   Should Mason's complain to this company ?   (*Explain*)

4. The journey times (in minutes) of a selection of trains travelling from Hillington East to Glasgow Central are shown below :-

| 5 | 8 | 9 | 8 | 6 | 7 | 10 | 7 | 7 | 5 | 9 | 5 | 7 | 8 | 8 | 20 | 5 |

a   What is the range of these times ?

b   Calculate the mean time for the journeys (correct to 1 decimal place).

c   One train took much longer than the mean time - which one ? - suggest a reason.

5. Competitive golfers use the mean when calculating their average number score for a tournament.

The winner of the latest competition scored a total of 273 for his 4 rounds.
Monty finished in second place, 3 shots behind.

a   What was Monty's total score ?

b   What was Monty's average score per round ?

c   If his average score per round had been 68, would he have won the tournament ? *Explain.*

6. In an ice-skating competition the marks given by the judges of eight countries were as follows :-

| 6·7 | 6·7 | 6·3 | 6·5 | 6·1 | 6·9 | 6·5 | 6·7 |

a   What was the range and the mean mark ?

b   How many marks above the mean was the highest mark awarded ?

7. Algi's say that their tins of sardines have the same number of fish in them. The weight of each tin is almost the same, but the number of sardines in each tin does tend to vary.

Here are the number of sardines which were found in tins bought by sardine lovers :-

| 8 | 5 | 10 | 5 | 9 | 6 | 8 | 8 | 6 | 8 | 16 | 6 | 9 |

a   Calculate the mean number of sardines per box and also state the range.

b   Relative to the mean, comment on the large number of sardines in one particular tin.

8. Anders likes fish and chips. He spent 6 days in his native Norway, eating his favourite dish in various chippies each day and recording how much he paid in £'s.

When he came to Scotland for 4 days he still insisted on fish and chips each day. Again, he recorded the price of his daily meal in different chippies.

The costs are shown in the table :-

Anders' Fish & Chips					
Norway	£9·50	£10·80	£8·60	£9·80	£8·30	£7·72
Scotland	£4·50	£4·75	£4·80	£4·95		

a   Calculate the mean cost for fish & chips in each country.

b   How much cheaper, on average, is fish & chips in Scotland than in Norway ?

The Median and the Mode

From a set of data, be able to find the median and the mode

In the previous exercise, you learned how to find the range of a set of numbers and how to calculate an average - namely the mean.

We now look at two further measures of average, - the median and the mode.

Median - The middle number, (*must put the numbers in order first*).

2, 3, 3, 3, 3, 5, 6, 7, 8, 9, 17

Median = 5

note :-
the numbers are in order.

Mode - The number that occurs most.

2, 3, 3, 3, 3, 5, 6, 7, 8, 9, 17

Mode = 3

there are four 3's

Don't Forget the Mean ...

Mean - Add all the data together and divide by the number of pieces of data.

$$\frac{2 + 3 + 3 + 3 + \dots + 9 + 17}{11} = 6$$

Exercise 7

1. Find the **range** and the **mode** for each set of data :-

   a 2, 3, 4, 5, 6, 7, 8, 8, 9

   b 12, 23, 14, 55, 12, 14, 32, 11, 14

   c 1·8, 2·2, 2·4, 1·5, 2·2, 6·1, 2·9

   d 80, 6, 80, 6, 80, 6, 80, 6, 80, 6, 80

   e 129, 208, 111, 122, 19, 118, 122

   f $\frac{2}{3}, \frac{1}{4}, \frac{3}{4}, \frac{4}{5}, \frac{3}{4}, \frac{1}{2}, \frac{3}{4}, \frac{1}{4}.$

2. Find the **median** for each set of data :- (Remember to put the numbers in order first).

   a 4, 7, 3, 1, 0, 5, 2, 8, 6

   b 12, 22, 15, 17, 28, 10, 16

   c 3·6, 4·2, 3·3, 4·4, 3, 3·7, 4·2

   d 152, 163, 106, 214, 185, 160, 198.

   If there is not a single middle number, take the **mean of the middle two numbers.**

   Example :-   2, 2, 4, (5, 6,) 7, 8, 10

   The median is (5 + 6) ÷ 2 = 5·5

3. Find the **median** for the following :-

   a 5, 12, 8, 9, 13, 8

   b 5, 7, 8, 16, 4, 18, 13, 9, 11, 10

   c 10, 6, 7, 5, 3, 6, 2, 9

   d 1·2, 1·3, 0·7, 1·6, 2·2, 1·5, 0·8, 1.

4. Look at the data set shown opposite :-

   a Find the range.   b Find the mean, median and mode.

   c Which **average** is best suited to this data set ?

   d Explain why you think the other two averages are less suitable.

   8, 9, 59, 10, 12, 4, 5, 6, 4.

5. The weights of six women are shown :–

| 65 kg | 75 kg | 88 kg | 65 kg | 72 kg | 74 kg. |

a Find the range of their weights.

b Calculate the mode and median weights.

c Choose which is the better average of those two and explain why.

6. Cindy buys 10 jars of jelly beans. The number of beans in each is listed below :–

| 108, | 107, | 109, | 106, | 108, | 107, | 108, | 111, | 105, | 111. |

a Calculate the mean, median and mode.

b How many jars contain more than the mean number of jelly beans ?

7. The heights of six men are shown opposite.

| 167 cm | 167 cm | 176 cm |
| 178 cm | 183 cm | 197 cm |

- Morag says - " the average height is 167 cm."
- Maureen says - " the average height is 178 cm."
- Mary says - " the average height is 177 cm."

a Explain why, technically, all three statements could be correct.

b Which of the three would be least likely to be used ?

8. Thirty pupils in Primary Seven were given a 30 word spelling test.

The teacher was to set a "pass" mark. Here are the marks out of 30 :–

18	21	23	19	24	25	17	20	18	18
17	22	20	25	22	19	16	21	22	16
18	23	24	19	15	18	24	23	30	29

a Rewrite the marks in order, starting at the lowest.

b Calculate the mean, median and mode and also find the range.

c If you were the teacher, what would your pass mark have been ? Give a reason !

9. The mean price of a 300 ml tube of toothpaste in 2 shops is £1·32.

If Superchem is selling it at £1·28, what must Semidrug's price be ?

10.

The mean age of these three diners is 42.
Henry is aged 46. Barry is 40.

What must Evelyn's age be ?

11. In a putting competition, the mean score for the first nine contestants was 27.
The next person to complete the course pulled the mean down to 26.

What must that 10th person have scored ?

Stem and Leaf Diagrams

Be able to interpret and construct a stem & leaf diagram

A stem and leaf diagram is yet another way of displaying information.

This ordered stem and leaf diagram shows the ages of people who joined Ferguston Bowling Club this summer.

The key explains what each number in the diagram represents.

The first line reads 21, 24, 26 and 29 years old.

Age in Years

2	1 4 6 9
3	3 6 8
4	3 3 3 4 6 7
5	0 2 6 9
6	0 4 5 5 8

stem   leaves

Key :-

3 | 8 means **38**

Exercise 8

1. From the above table, it can be seen that those in their thirties are aged 33, 36 and 38.

   a   Write down the ages of those in their :-   (i) forties   (ii) fifties.

   b   What is the age of the oldest person to join ?

   c   How many people who joined are aged :-   (i) 43   (ii) 57 ?

   d   How many people are over the age of 45 ?

   e   How many people joined altogether in the summer ?

2. The ages of people waiting in a queue at a theme park are shown in the stem and leaf diagram opposite.

   a   How many people in the queue are in their

      (i) thirties   (ii) fifties ?

   b   What age is the youngest person ?

   c   What is the difference in ages between the youngest and oldest person (range).

   d   Which age appears most often (mode).

   e   How many people are in the queue at the theme park ?

   f   Why are there no leaves in the 4th line ?

Age in Years

1	0 2 4 4 4 6
2	1 2 7
3	2 2 4 6 7 8
4	
5	0 1 1 3 6 7

Key :-

2 | 7 means **27**

3. This stem and leaf diagram shows the response when a group of young ladies were asked how long (minutes) they spent each day on keeping fit.

   a   Write a key for this diagram.   b   How many were asked ?

   c   What's the modal time ?   d   Find the median.

Keep Fit Time

0	7 8 8 8 8 9
1	0 3 5
2	3 3 3 4 6 9
3	5 5
4	0 0 0 2 5 5

4. A group of children were asked how many burgers they had eaten in the past month.

The stem and leaf graph shows the results.

Burgers

Key :-
3|6 means **36**

0	0 0 1 6
1	1 4 4 4
2	0 1 1 2 5 7
3	6 9
4	0 0 3

a Write down each amount in order, smallest number first.

b What amount of burgers appears most often (mode).

c How many children ate no burgers ?

d How many children were asked ?

e Work out the median number of burgers eaten.

5. The race times, in minutes, for the under-fifteen Bishopton Fun Run were recorded in an **unordered** stem and leaf diagram.

Fun Run Times

If this **unordered** diagram was rearranged to form an **ordered** stem and leaf diagram the first line would read as :-

Key :-
5|2 means **52**

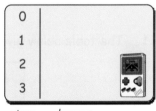

2	8 1 8 2 7
3	5 0 2 8 6 3
4	9 5 6 3 7
5	2 0
6	2 0 1

$$2 \mid 1 \ 2 \ 7 \ 8 \ 8$$

a Write out the 2nd line in order.

b Redo the stem and leaf diagram with all the lines in order.

c Find the modal time, the median time and the range of times.

d How many of the under-fifteens took over an hour to complete the fun run ?

6. HVM have only 12 computer games left in their sale.

Their prices are shown in a table.

Copy the diagram with the stem and put in the leaves to make it an **ordered** stem and leaf diagram.

(Remember to give it a key).

£7 £22 £16 £12
£33 £8 £20 £19
£14 £23 £8 £25

0	
1	
2	
3	

stem   leaves

7.

12	17	46	46	37	11
8	16	29	30	46	49
14	50	20	33	47	14
24	35	47	23	18	5

A teacher recorded the marks (out of 60) for a History test.

Construct an ordered stem and leaf graph using the information.

8. This table shows how long (in seconds) a group of teenagers were able to hold their breath under water.

15	25	12	30	42	61	19
51	37	23	48	57	18	23
16	48	26	61	37	19	61
35	26	43	21	54	60	15

a Construct an ordered stem and leaf diagram.

b How many managed over 30 seconds ?

c Find the range, mode and median time.

9. For the two sets of data below :-

    a   Construct an ordered stem and leaf diagram   b   Find the range

    c   Write down the mode   d   Calculate the median.

(i)

126	151	162	173	102	132	166	157	170	111	116	128
112	133	126	165	117	123	150	160	128	143	140	151
131	128	164	156	121	168	140	153	162	167	104	175

(ii)

3·5	2·4	4·7	1·8	5·7	4·5	1·2	4·0	5·3	6·2	6·8	4·2
2·9	2·7	1·4	2·4	6·5	5·2	1·1	4·5	2·3	3·4	5·1	0·6
5·0	2·8	4·8	2·3	5·2	4·7	5·2	6·3	2·5	5·8	5·9	1·1

10. This question shows a back-to-back stem and leaf diagram, giving the age and gender of people at a wedding.

    a   Explain what you think - 9 9 6 3 | 1 | 2 6 8 means.

    b   How many males at the wedding are aged :-

        (i) 19   (ii) 33   (iii) 50 ?

    c   Find the modal age and median age of :-

        (i)   the males (ii) the females.

    d   How many people were at the wedding ?

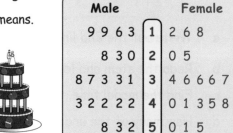

Age of People

Male		Female
9 9 6 3	1	2 6 8
8 3 0	2	0 5
8 7 3 3 1	3	4 6 6 6 7
3 2 2 2 2	4	0 1 3 5 8
8 3 2	5	0 1 5

11. The table below gives the ages of a few men and women when they got married.

Men	23 35 45 32 19 23 33 37
Women	22 18 19 23 27 27 30 29

    a   Draw an ordered back to back stem and leaf diagram to represent this information.

    b   Find the modal and median ages of :-   (i) the men   (ii) the women.

12. a   Draw an ordered back to back stem and leaf diagram showing the details about the heights (*in centimetres*) of the players in two football teams.

Pollock	148 156 172 181 160 157 164 132 184 146 157 139
Ashfield	182 174 138 145 175 162 159 175 167 173 144 150

    b   Find the modal and median heights of :- (i) Pollock   (ii) Ashfield.

    c   Write a few sentences comparing the mode and the median of both teams.

Conducting a Survey Properly

Be able to carry out an unbiased survey and analyse the results

A statistician is a mathematician who specialises in research into various aspects of human life and very often has to carry out surveys.

Discuss :-

When setting up a survey, preparation is very important.

Have you avoided bias in your survey ? (What is bias ?)

Will you use a tally box or a questionnaire ?

Will you use discrete (countable) or continuous (measurable) data.

What form will the final information take ?

How will you analyse and present your results ?

Hi. I'm taking a survey.

Exercise 9

1. Barry is to conduct a survey asking whether or not a local weekend disco should be closed down.
    Explain why he should not ask the following groups :-

    a   The staff of the disco.

    b   People leaving the disco at 3 a.m. on Saturday morning.

    c   The old folks home across the road.

2. Construct a questionnaire to allow several responses to the following surveys :-

    a   How much would you spend each week on magazines ?

    b   On average, how many hours sleep do you get each weekend ?

    c   Approximately how many kilometres do you travel to school each day ?

3. Describe each sentence below using either the words discrete or continuous.

    a   The number of pets each person has in a class.

    b   The distances pupils walk to school.

    c   The temperatures at noon everyday for a week.

    d   Time taken by runners in a 100 metre race.

4. Conduct a survey by asking the class how many pets they have.
    Use in your final results three separate methods of displaying the information.

5. a   Conduct a survey of your choosing, using a group of 50 people.

    b   Your survey should be of a numerical nature. (Not favourite colour etc.).

    c   Use three separate graphical methods of displaying your information.

    d   Analyse your data (mean, median, mode, range) and give a written report.

    e   Explain why you chose your subject matter and any other relevant details.

Revisit - Review - Revise

1. A survey was carried out in a sweetie shop, where children were asked to name their favourite Hiribo jelly sweet

   a   How many chose Jelly Frogs ?

   b   How many more chose Jelly Worms than Jelly Gummy Bears ?

   c   How many less chose Jelly Fried Eggs than Jelly Babies ?

   d   How many were asked altogether ?

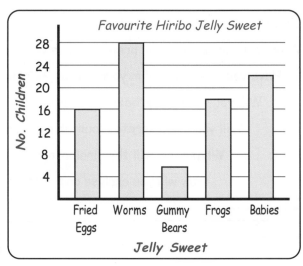

Favourite Hiribo Jelly Sweet

2.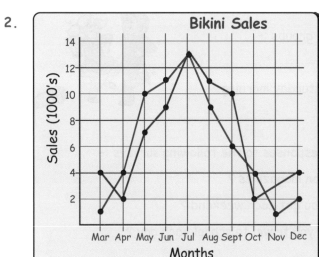

   Bikini Sales

   The line graph shows the number of bikinis sold by two swimwear companies over a period of 10 months.

   Swimsport's sales are shown in red.

   Paddlepro's sales are in green.

   a   In which month did sales peak for both companies ? Why this month ?

   b   Who sold more bikinis in May - how many more ?

   c   Which company had the biggest fall in sales between two months - which two months was that ?

   d   Overall, who sold more bikini's over the period ?

   e   Suggest a reason for an increase in sales by both companies later in the year.

3. In a garden centre survey, 240 people were asked which method they preferred to get rid of weeds in their garden.

   The results are shown in the pie chart.

   a   What angle at the centre is taken up by Watering Can ?

   b   How many people preferred :-

      (i)   to use a spray   (ii)   to burn the weeds ?

   c   How many preferred to put weedkiller down using a watering can ?

   How to do away with weeds

   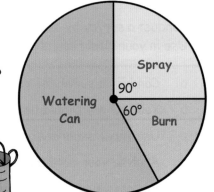

4. Joe went online to find the price he would have to pay to renew the two front tyres on his car.

   He found 20 garages around where he lives which had the tyres he needed in stock.

   Here were the prices :- £153   £168   £174   £200   £190   £180   £200   £168   £174   £187

                         £180   £196   £153   £174   £185   £190   £163   £202   £181   £174

   a   Construct an **ordered stem-and-leaf** diagram, including a **key**.

   b   What is the **modal** price of the tyres ?

   c   Determine the **median** price.

5. The table shows the eye colour of children in a Secondary 1 class.

Eye colour	Number	Fraction	Angle
Brown	10	$\frac{10}{30}$	$\frac{10}{30}$ x 360 = ...°
Blue	12		x 360 = ...°
Green	7		x 360 = ...°
Grey	1		x 360 = ...°
TOTAL	**?**		**360°**

   a   How many children are in the class ?

   b   Copy and complete the table.

   c   Construct a neat accurate **pie chart** to show the information.

6. Thistle Holidays are promoting end of season short holidays.

Month	For 4 Nights					Over 4 Nights
	2 adults	Each extra adult	Each young adult 13 - 16	Each child aged 5 - 12	Each child aged 0 - 4	Each additional night per family
Oct	£195	£68	£50	Free	Free	£20
Nov	£175	£60	£40	£15	Free	£15
Dec	£299	£80	£60	£30	Free	£35

Calculate the cost of :-

   a   A 4 night holiday for 3 adults and 2 children aged 3 and 14 in November.

   b   A 5 night holiday for 2 adults, a 13 and 15 year old and a 6 year old in December.

   c   Suggest a reason why December prices are a bit higher.

7. Find the **range** of these numbers :- 87, 29, 58, 25, 88, 19, 39, 15, 18.

8. Determine the **mode** for these lengths (metres) :-

   8 m, 9 m, 8 m, 10 m, 9 m, 8 m, 8 m, 9 m, 12 m, 9 m, 12 m, 9 m, 12 m.

9. Find the **median** temperature :-

   5°C, –4°C, 2°C, 8°C, –6°C, 6°C, 10°C, –18°C, 5°C, 3°C.

10. Calculate the **mean** weight (grams) :-

   60 g, 50 g, 150 g, 80 g, 100 g, 110 g, 40 g, 70 g.

11.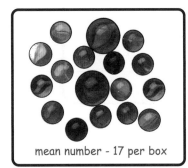

   mean number - 17 per box

   The contents of ten boxes of marbles are examined.

   The boxes have the following number of marbles :-

   16, 18, 14, 17, 15, 16, 15, 15, 18, 16.

   a   Why is the manufacturer's claim wrong ?

   b   An eleventh box is examined. How many marbles would need to be in that box in order for the manufacturer's claim to **then** be considered to be correct ?

12. Shown is the number of cartons of juice bought by two mums over a number of weeks.

Tina	3	5	3	3	3	6	4	3	7
Anne	2	4	4	5	2	3	4	4	5

   a   Write down the **modal** amount bought by each mum.

   b   Give a reason why it is unfair to compare their purchases by using the mode.

13. Here are the prices shown by ten garages for a litre of petrol.

   £1·45, £1·50, £1·55, £1·46, £1·50, £1·51, £1·53, £1·55, £1·45, £1·50.

   Find the mode, the median and the mean price.

14.

   The **mean** age of 5 boys is 15 years old.

   Four of the them are aged 13, 14, 16 and 19.

   What is the age of the other one ?

REVIEW 12

Time

1. Write down the **formula** for finding :-

   a   **Distance**, given the speed you were travelling at and the time taken.

   b   **Average Speed**, given distance travelled and time taken.

   c   **Time**, given distance travelled and the speed you were travelling at.

2. Daphne took 2 hours to type 4800 words.

   What was her typing speed, in words **per minute**.

3.  A train, travelling at a steady speed of 160 km/hr took $8\frac{1}{2}$ hours to complete its journey.

   How far had it travelled ?

4. A coach travelled the 448 km from Dundee to Birmingham at an average speed of 80 km/hr.

   How long did the journey take, in hours and minutes ?

5. 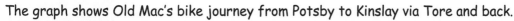 A tall ship travelled 4·5 miles downwind in 15 minutes.

   What speed did it average ?

6. Express :-

   a   4 hours 36 minutes in hours only   b   3·8 hours as hours and minutes

   c   30 metres per second as kilometres per hour.

7. The graph shows Old Mac's bike journey from Potsby to Kinslay via Tore and back.

   a   At what time did Mac's journey begin ?

   b   How far is it from :-

      (i) Potsby to Tore

      (ii) Tore to Kinslay ?

   c   How long did it take him from Tore to Kinslay ?

   d   How far did he travel in the last half hour of the trip ?

   e   Calculate his average speed from Potsby to Tore.

   f   Work out his average speed from Kinslay back to Potsby.

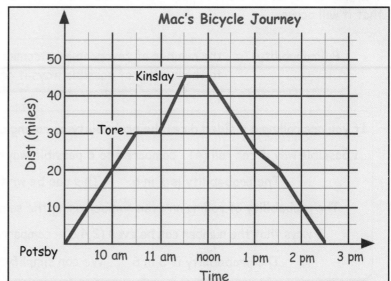

CHAPTER 13 Probability

Be able to judge
sensibly when
making a choice

Making a Choice

For discussion :- Which of these events are fair and which are not fair ?

- When playing the game of Noughts and Crosses, the same player always starts first.

- The fastest runner, who enters a race, is asked to run further than the others.

- You toss a coin to decide which team bats first in a game of cricket.

- A bag contains 3 red balls and 7 green balls.
  You must pick a red ball to win.

- A man races a child in a 50 metre swimming pool.

Exercise 1

1. Liz and Ted, are playing a game of Rock - Paper - Scissors.

    a   Make a list of the 3 possible choices Liz could make.

    b   There are 9 possible combinations for each game. What are they ?

    c   Play the game with a partner 18 times. Record how many times each player wins.

    d   If it is a game of chance, how many times should each child win ?

Probability Expressed in Ratio Form

Be able to
express
probability
in ratio form

The probability of an event happening is a measure of how likely it is that it will occur.

> P (Probability) = the number of favourable outcomes compared
> to the number of possible ways it can occur.

If you are rolling a 6 sided dice, the probability of rolling a 4 is found as follows :-

1 possible way it can roll (4) - compared to 6 possible ways it can happen (1,2,3,4,5,6).

The probability is 1 in 6.   This can be written as   P(4) = 1 in 6.

The probability of rolling an even number using the same dice is :-

3 ways that the number can be even (2,4,6) - compared to the 6 possible outcomes.

The probability is 3 in 6.   We can simplify this to   P(even) = 1 in 2.

1. A jar has 1 green, 5 red and 4 blue marbles in it.

   If a marble is chosen at random, find these probabilities :-

   a   P(green)   b   P(red)   c   P(blue)   d   P(black).

2. 2 coins are tossed at the same time.

   One possibility is there will be **two heads** showing (H, H).

   a   List all 4 possible ways the two coins could land.

   b   What is the probability of two heads showing ? (H, H).

   c   What is the probability of two tails showing ?

   d   What is the probability of a head and a tail showing ?

   e   What is the probability of any other combination showing ?

3. These number cards are placed in a box and taken out at random.

   a   Which number has the **greatest** chance of being chosen ? Why ?

   b   Which number has the **least** chance of being chosen ? Why ?

   c   What is the probability that the card with 3 on it will be chosen ?

   d   If you take 4 cards from the box are you guaranteed of choosing at least one 5 ?

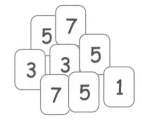

4. Roll a 6 sided dice 30 times and record the results.

   a   Draw a graph to show how often each number shows.

   b   What does your graph show ?

   c   How many times do you think each number 1 to 6 should turn up in the 30 throws of your dice ?

   d   Compare your results to the others in your class. What did you find ?

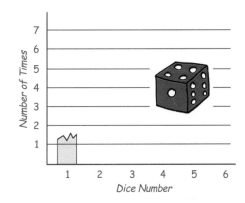

5. In a bowl of fruit there are 3 oranges, 2 apples and 5 bananas.

   a   One is chosen at random. Find :-

   (i)   P(an orange)   (ii)   P(an apple)   (iii)   P(a banana)   (iv)   P(a pear).

   b   If, when I choose one of the fruits I always put it back each time, how many times would I expect to get :-

   (i)   an orange from 10 picks   (ii)   an apple from 50 picks

   (iii)   a banana from 100 picks   (iv)   a pear from 30 picks ?

6. When a red dice and a green dice
   are rolled a combination of pairings
   can be set up to show all the possible outcomes.

   $(1, 1)$ $(1, 2)$ $(1, 3)$ $(1, 4)$ $(1, \_)$ $(1, \_)$
   $(2, 1)$ $(2, 2)$ $(\ ,\ )$ $(\ ,\ )$ $(\ ,\ )$ $(\ ,\ )$
   $(\ ,\ )$ ....

   a   Copy the first few combinations shown
       and complete the list to show them all.

   ....

   If the two numbers in each combination
   are then added we get all the totals from 2 to 12.

   b   How many different combinations
       of pairings can you get ?

   c   Copy the table and complete it to
       show all the possible totals of the
       combinations.

Dice 1 / Dice 2	1	2	3	4	5	6
1	2	3	4			
2	3	4				
3	4					
4						
5						
6						

   The probability of a total score of **3** is :- **2 in 36**.
   (there are 2 ways out of 36 possible combinations).

    This simplifies to :- **1 in 18**.

   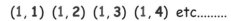

   d   What is the **most likely** total to get when you roll 2 dice ? Why ?

   e   What is the **least likely** total ? Why ?

   f   What is the probability, (*simplify as far as possible*), of scoring a total of :-

       (i)   2   (ii)   4   (iii)   7   (iv)   10   (v)   1 ?

   g   What is the probability of scoring :-

       (i)   a total higher than 8   (ii)   a double e.g. (2, 2) ?

7. A six-sided dice is rolled and a four-sided spinner is spun at the same time.

   a   Write down all possible combinations of pairings. How many are there ?

                $(1, 1)$ $(1, 2)$ $(1, 3)$ $(1, 4)$ etc.........

   b   Construct a table, similar to question 1, to show all the possible totals of the combinations.

   c   What is the probability, (*simplify as far as possible*), of scoring a total of :-

       (i)   3   (ii)   5   (iii)   7   (iv)   8 ?

   d   What is the probability of scoring :-

       (i)   a total lower than 6   (ii)   a total higher than 8 ?

8. A five-sided spinner and an eight-sided spinner are spun at the same time.

   a   Write down all possible combinations of pairings.

   b   Construct a table to show all the possible totals of the combinations.

   c   What is the probability, (*simplify as far as possible*), of scoring a total of :-

       (i)   6   (ii)   10   (iii)   12   (iv)   13   (v)   more than 11 ?

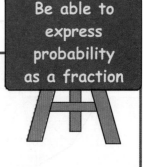

Be able to express probability as a fraction

We can also use fractions between 0 and 1 to show the probability that something will happen.

This spinner has 8 coloured sections, equal in size.

The probability that it will land on blue is given by :-

$$P(\text{blue}) = \frac{\text{number of blue sections}}{\text{total number of sections}} = \frac{4}{8} = \frac{1}{2}$$

$$P(\text{purple}) = \frac{\text{number of purple sections}}{\text{total number of sections}} = \frac{1}{8}$$

$$P(\text{green}) = \frac{\text{number of green sections}}{\text{total number of sections}} = \frac{3}{8}$$

* Note that the probability it will land on any colour $= \frac{8}{8} = 1$ (a certainty).

The probability that it will land on an orange colour section = 0 (an impossibility).

Exercise 3   *Answer in the simplest form, where possible.*

1. A bag contains 5 yellow balls and 10 red balls.

    A ball is chosen at random. What is the probability that it will be yellow ?

2.  A box of chocolates has 8 strawberry creams and 12 coffee creams.

    If a chocolate is chosen at random, what is the probability that it will be a coffee cream ?

3. A six sided dice numbered 1 to 6 is rolled.

    a   What is the probability it will show a two ? Record it as P(2) = ...

    b   What is the probability it will show a four ? P(4) = ...

    c   What is the probability it will show an odd number ? P(odd) = ...

    d   What is the probability it will show a number bigger than 1 ? P(> 1) =...

    e   What is the probability it will show an eight ? P(8) = ...

4. The names of 12 boys and 18 girls are put into a draw for the remaining school disco ticket.

    If a name is chosen at random, what is the probability that it will be :-

    a   a boy's name   b   a girl's name ?

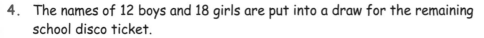

5.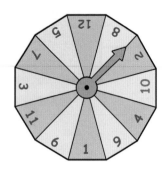

A 12 sided spinner is spun until it stops on a number.

Find the following probabilities :-

a   P(7)   b   P(even)

c   P(multiple of 4)   d   P(two digit number)

e   P(prime number).

6. At a school fete, people throw a 50 pence coin onto a grid to win a prize.

If a coin actually lands **on a square** on the board, what is the probability the person :-

a   will lose   b   will win a prize

c   will win £1   d   will win £5

e   will end up with less than their initial stake ?

lose	£1	lose	£1
lose	25p	lose	£1
£5	lose	20p	lose
lose	50p	lose	75p

7. In a word game, letters are chosen at random from the word :-

P   E   T   E   R   H   E   A   D

Work out the following probabilities :-

a   P(T)   b   P(E)   c   P(vowel)   d   P(not a vowel).

8. A pack of standard playing cards contains 52 cards (see below).

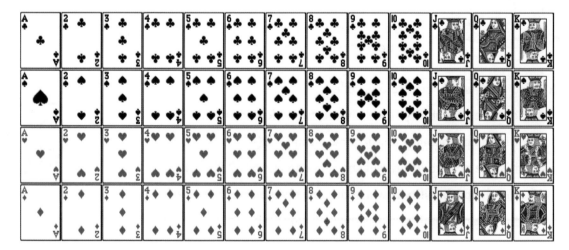

A card is chosen at random. What is the probability that it will be :-

a   black   b   red   c   a spade

d   an ace   e   King of hearts   f   a face card

g   smaller than 6   h   red or black   i   a joker ?

9.  A farmer has 4 white, 6 black and 20 brown cows in a shed that need to be milked.

   What is the probability the first cow through the gate will be :-

   a   white   b   brown   c   not black ?

10. A plastic bag holds 13 cans of diet cola and 12 cans of regular cola.

    a   If a can is chosen at random, what is the probability that it will be diet cola ?

    b   If that diet cola can is **not** put back into the bag, what is the probability that the **next** can chosen will be regular cola ?

11. A bag contains 5 discs, numbered 1, 2, 3, 4 and 5.

    Mandy takes a disc at random from the bag.

    She notes the number and puts the disc back.

    She shakes the bag and picks again.

    She adds this number to the first number.

1st No. \ 2nd No.	1	2	3	4	5
1					
2					
3				7	
4					
5					

    a   Copy and complete the table to show all possible totals.

    b   Calculate the probability that Mandy's total is :-

    (i)   8   (ii)   10   (iii)   1   (iv)   3 or 4.

12. Three 2p coins are tossed at the same time.

    a   Write down all possible combinations of the outcomes.

    b   How many are there in total ?

    c   Write down the probability that there will be :-

    (H H H),   (H T H),

    (H T T), ...

    (i)   three heads   (ii)   2 of one kind and one of the other

    (iii)   only one tail   (iv)   3 coins all the same.

13. The probability of choosing a page from a newspaper with no adverts in it is known to be 0·15.

    If there are 60 pages in this newspaper, how many pages don't have any adverts ?

14. Andy was told that the probability of him choosing a white chocolate truffle, his favourite, from a box of continental truffles was 0·4.

    When he counted, he discovered there were 8 white truffles in the box.

    How many truffles were there in the box altogether ?

Be able to work
out probability in
independent events

Independent Events

Two events are **independent** if the fact that A occurs **does
not** affect the probability of B occurring.

- Landing on a Head when tossing a coin and rolling a 6 on a dice.

- Choosing a Queen from a pack of cards, replacing it, and then choosing an Ace.

Example :- A cupboard contains 4 pairs of shoes - brown, black, red and white.
Without looking, you reach into the cupboard and choose a pair.
You put that pair back into the cupboard and choose a second pair.

What's the probability that you will choose a brown pair both times ?

$$P(\text{brown}) = \tfrac{1}{4} \Rightarrow P(\text{brown \& brown}) = P(\text{brown}) \times P(\text{brown}) = \tfrac{1}{4} \times \tfrac{1}{4} = \tfrac{1}{16}$$

Rule :- When 2 events, A and B, are independent, the probability of both occurring is :-

$$P(A \text{ and } B) = P(A) \times P(B)$$

Exercise 4

1. A coin is tossed at the same time as a 6-sided dice is rolled.

    Find the probability of a tail **and** the number 4 appearing.

2. A card is chosen at random from a pack of 52 cards.
    It is then replaced and a second card is chosen.

    What is the probability of choosing a King and then a Ten ?

3. A jar contains 3 red, 5 green, 2 blue and 6 yellow marbles.
    A marble is chosen at random from the jar.
    After replacing it, a second marble is chosen.

    What is the probability of choosing a green followed by a yellow marble ?

4. A Xmas tree has 6 green baubles, 3 red baubles, 5 white baubles and 7 yellow.
    Two baubles are chosen from the tree, with replacement.

    What is the probability that both baubles chosen are red ?

5. Four cards are chosen from a standard pack of 52 playing cards with replacement.

    What is the probability of choosing four Clubs in a row ?

6. Spin a spinner numbered 1 to 9 and also toss a coin.

    What is the probability of getting an Even number on the spinner and a Head on the coin ?

Dependent Events

Two events are dependent if the outcome of the first affects the outcome of the second so that the probability is changed.

Example :-   A card is chosen at random from a pack of 52 playing cards.
Without replacing it, a 2nd card is chosen.

What is the probability that the first card chosen is a Queen and the 2nd card chosen is an Ace ?

> P(queen on 1st pick) $= \frac{4}{52}$
>
> P(ace on 2nd pick without queen on 1st pick) $= \frac{4}{51}$
>
> P(queen & ace) $= \frac{4}{52} \times \frac{4}{51} = \frac{16}{2652} = \frac{4}{663}$

> Rule :-   When 2 events, A and B, are dependent, the probability of both occurring is :-
>
> P(A and B) = P(A) × P(B without A)

Exercise 5

 ✓

1. Two cards are chosen at random from a pack of 52 cards without replacement.

    What is the probability they are both hearts ?

2. Two cards are chosen at random from a pack without replacement.

    What is the probability that the first card is a four and the second card is a nine ?

3. Three cards are chosen at random from a pack without replacement.

    What is the probability of choosing a Jack, a Queen and a King in that order ?

4.    A school buys 20 printers, but 4 are faulty.
    Three printers are randomly chosen and tested.

    What is the probability all three are the ones which don't work if the first and second ones are not replaced after being tested ?

5. In a Higher English exam, 5 out of 25 students got an "A" pass.

    If three students are picked out at random without replacement, what is the probability that all three got an "A" in the exam ?

6.    A school survey found that 7 out of 10 pupils walk to school.

    If four pupils are selected at random without replacement, what is the probability that all four walk to school ?

1. A plastic bag contains 7 chillies, 9 beetroot and 11 carrots.

   a   If one of these is picked at random, what is the probability it will be a beetroot ?

   b   If it is a beetroot and is **not** put back into the bag, what is the probability that the next item out will be a chilli ?

2. A group of over forty's were asked how they dried their hair.

   The results are shown in the table.

   What is the probability, (simplest form), that a person chosen at random from this sample will :-

   a   use a hair dryer

   b   be male and use a towel ?

Gender \ Method	Towel	Dryer
Female	20	90
Male	60	30

3. In a baker's shop, the probability that an iced doughnut will remain in stock by the end of the day is known to be 0·2.

   One day, there were 10 iced doughnuts left at closing time.

   How many must there have been in the shop that day to begin with ?

4.    The probability of your purchase being stuck in a vending machine is 0·004.

   If a vending machine is used 5000 times per year, how many times should you expect to be unlucky and have a need to complain ?

5. Two five-sided spinners were spun at the same time.

   By writing out all the combinations, calculate the probability of getting :-

   a   a **double 2**

   b   a **total of 6 or less** from both spinners.

6.    A purse contains 2 fifty pence coins, 4 twenty pence coins and a few ten pence coins.

   One of the coins is chosen at random.

   The probability of a 10p coin being chosen is $\frac{1}{4}$.

   How many 10 pences must there be in the purse ?

7. A jar contains 20 red, 30 green, 10 blue and 5 yellow jelly beans.

   A jelly bean is chosen at random from the jar.

   After **replacing** it, a second bean is chosen.

   What is the probability of choosing a red and then a yellow jelly bean ?

CHAPTER 14

Revision

Revise all work covered in CfE Level 3

Revision of ALL CfE Level 3 Work

Do NOT use a calculator except where you see the sign.

1. Round to 3 decimal places :-　　　a　2·4156　　　b　0·008 499.

2. Round to 2 significant figures :-　　　a　9·867　　　b　4 648 720.

3. How many significant figures does the number 0·009 200 have ?

4. By rounding, find an **approximate** answer to 78 450 ÷ 179.

5. A farmer's crop of 70 kg of potatoes is sealed into 3·5 kg plastic bags.
   He sells the bags at £1·50 each. How much money will he make ?

6. A 42" TV set was on sale for £480·00. I bought it using a hire purchase agreement :-
   - I paid an initial deposit of 25% of the cash price
   - I then made 10 payments of £39·50 each
   a　How much did it cost me paying it up this way ?
   b　How much would I have saved if I had paid cash ?

7. Find :-　　　a　41 × 300　　　b　66400 ÷ 80.

8. What is the answer to :-　　　a　5 + 2 × 3　　　b　15 - 10 ÷ 5 + 3 ?

9. Find :-　　a　(-10) - 4　　b　15 - (-12)　　c　69 + (-70)
   　　　　　d　(8) × (-4)　　e　(-45) ÷ (-5)　　f　$(-1)^7$.

10. Find the **lowest common multiple** of :-　　　a　8 and 6　　　b　4, 5 and 6.

11. Find the **highest common factor** of :-　　　a　24 and 42　　　b　21, 42 and 63.

12. List all the **prime** numbers between 50 and 80.

13. As a **product of its prime factors**, 60 can be written as 2 × 2 × 3 × 5.
    Write the number 56 as a **product of its prime factors**.

14. Find :-   a 5^2 b 20^2 c 3^3

              d 5^4 e $\sqrt{64}$ f $\sqrt{900}$.

15. Change to a **decimal** :-   a $\frac{3}{5}$ b   3%.

16. Change to a **percentage** :-   a   0·2   b $\frac{3}{4}$.

17. Find :-   a   50% of £170   b   20% of £3·50   c $12\frac{1}{2}$ % of $40.

18. A greenhouse is priced at £1200.

    In a sale, a **discount** of 5% is given.

    How much would I pay for the greenhouse in the sale ?

19.    The Gaiety Theatre was having a refit and the seating
    capacity was **increased** by 30%.

    The old theatre had an original audience of 450 .

    How many can the revamped theatre hold ?

20. Find :-   a $\frac{1}{4}$ + $\frac{1}{3}$ b $2\frac{3}{4}$ + $3\frac{5}{8}$ c $6\frac{1}{3}$ – $4\frac{3}{5}$.

21. Change :-   a $3\frac{5}{6}$ to a **top heavy fraction**   b $\frac{21}{4}$ to a **mixed number**.

22. If a lift takes 33 seconds to climb 6 floors, how long will it take to climb 1 floor ?

23. 1 chocolate chip cookie costs 45p. I got a pack of 8 for £3.

    Had I received a discount ? (*Explain*).

    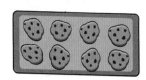

24. 5 trips to the dump with my car when clearing out my loft took 2 hours 5 minutes.

    How much **longer** would an extra 3 trips take ?

25. Which is the better buy here ?

    The 700 ml bottle of olive oil or the 2 litre can ?

    (*Explain*).

    £6·30   £16·00

26.

Georgio is a waiter in a hotel and earns £12 per hour.

He was called in at the weekend to help at a wedding.

Overtime is paid at **time and a half**.

Over the weekend, he put in 12 hours overtime.

How much was he paid for his weekend overtime work ?

27. Avril is a primary teacher. Her **gross** monthly pay is £2350.

Her monthly deductions are Income Tax - £370,

National Insurance - £115 and Graduated Pension - £108.

What is Avril's **net** monthly pay ?

28. a   A truck covers 260 miles in 4 hours. What is the truck's **average speed** ?

   b   The Hubble telescope travels round the earth at 7·5 km/second.

   How **far** will it fly in 8 seconds at this speed ?

   c   A car is towed at a steady speed of 40 km/hr.

   How **long** will it take it to cover a distance of 90 km ?

29. Shown is a graph indicating how far a plane travels as it flies from Edinburgh to Athens in Greece.

Calculate the **average speed** of the plane.

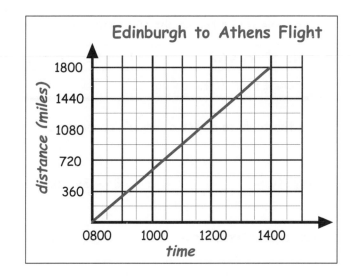

30. Calculate the **area** of each of these shapes :-

a

7 cm

10 cm

b

5 m

6 m

kite

31. Calculate the **circumference** of this no entry sign.

It has a **radius** of 50 centimetres.

32. 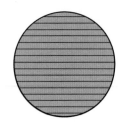 The **diameter** of this circular wooden lid is 20 cm.

Calculate the **area** of the lid.

33. Calculate the **capacity** of this water tank in litres.

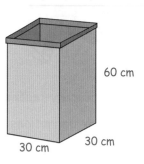

60 cm

30 cm   30 cm

34. 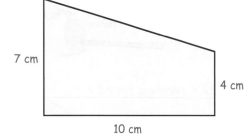 Calculate the **area** of this shape.

7 cm

4 cm

10 cm

35. Write the next **two** numbers in the following sequences :-

a   187, 178, 169, 160, ..., ...   b   2, 6, 12, 20, ..., ...   c   1, 1, 2, 3, 5, 8, 13, ..., ...

36. This table shows the height of a tomato plant over a 5 day period.

No. of day's (d)	1	2	3	4	5
Height in cm (H)	15	21	27	33	39

Use the table to devise a **formula** connecting H and d.

37. Simplify :-   a $8x - 3y - 5x + 10y$ b $5a \times 4b$.

38. Multiply out brackets :-   a $2m(3m - 2n)$ b $-4(3x - 5y)$.

39. **Simplify** fully :- $9t + 6s - 3(t - 4s)$.

40. If $p = 13$, $q = 4$ and $r = -3$, find the value of $\dfrac{p - r}{2q}$.

41. Solve :-   a $3x - 2 = 16$ b $6x + 5 = 3x + 29$

                         c $4(2x - 3) = x + 2$ d $\frac{1}{2}x - 9 = 13$.

42. Solve these inequalities :- a $5x - 2 > 28$ b $\frac{1}{3}x + 7 \leqslant 22$.

43.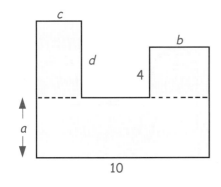

a Write down a formula for the area (*A*) of this shape in terms of *a, b, c* and *d*.

b Evaluate the formula given :-

   a = 3·5, *b* = 4·5, *c* = 3 and *d* = 6.

44. Find the value of the angle marked ∗ in each of these figures :-

a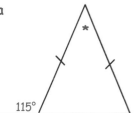

b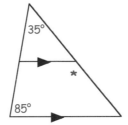

c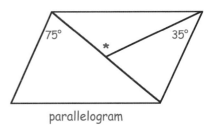

parallelogram

45. What is the compass direction for the 3 figure bearing 225° ?

46. As the captain of a ship sails on a bearing of 050°, he notices another ship going in the exact opposite direction. On what bearing must the 2nd ship be heading ?

47. This drawing of Cologne Cathedral was done to a scale :-

   1 cm represents 40 metres.

   What is the real height of the cathedral ?

   4 cm

48.

6 cm

5 cm

Shown is an umbrella and a photograph of it.

Calculate the scale factor and use it to determine the span (*h* cm) of the blue nylon part of the umbrella.

49.

a Write down the coordinates of point P.

b Write down the coordinates of a 4th point S such that PQRS is a rhombus.

c Point R is reflected over the dotted line to point R'. Write the coordinates of R'.

50. State (**yes** or **no**) which of these shapes would **tile** a flat surface ?

a  b 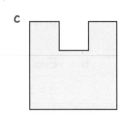 c d e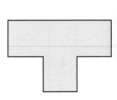

51. Here are the bank balances of a group of students.

£50, £20, -£10, £50, -£20, £110, £80, £20, -£50, £50.

a What is the **range** of the bank balances ?   b What is the **modal balance** ? (*the mode*).

c What is the **median** balance ?   d What is the **mean** balance ?

52. Jen's **mean** mark out of 3 tests was 58.

She scored 62 in English and 36 in French.

What must Jen's mark have been in her Maths test ?

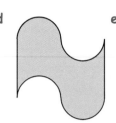

53. Four finals in the Olympics were being shown on TV at the same time.

The **pie chart** shows which sport a group of women chose to watch.

a What **fraction** of the women chose to watch the 100 m race ?

b If 180 women took part in the survey, **how many** of them watched the 100 m race ?

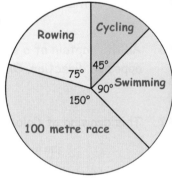

54.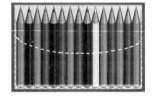

This pack contains 1 yellow, 3 blue, 5 red and 6 green pencils.

What, in its simplest form, is the **probability** the first pencil chosen from the pack is green ?

55. From a group of people, the number wearing glasses is noted.

The probability of choosing one from the group who is actually wearing glasses is 0·25.

In fact, 5 from the group were wearing glasses.

How many were **not** wearing glasses ?

56. **Copy** this shape and **rotate** it by a half turn around the red dot.

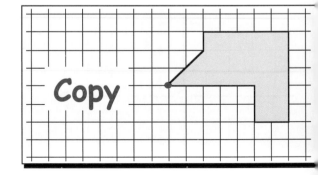

answers to Book 3b

Answers to Chapter 0 (page 1)

1. a 4000   b 200000
2. a 68000   b 0·99
3. a 127000   b 0·0622
4. a 3   b 2   c 5
5. a 16000   b 800000   c 60
    d 300   e 300   c 0·2
6. 8499
7. a 930   b 846000   c 161200
    d 220   e 2000   f 1400
8. a 10   b 17   c 4
9. a (7 + 2) x 4 = 36
    b 15 ÷ (5 - 2) = 5
    c (7 + 8) ÷ (2 + 3) = 3
10. 2 adults and 6 children
11. a 105°   b 15°
12. a 59°   b 45°   c 25°
    d 70°   e 139°, 41°, 41°
    f 50°   g 68°, 44°
    h 73°, 73°   i 40°, 40°, 100°
13. a -3   b 2   c 7
    d 10   e -3   f 10
    g 0   h -3
14. a 0   b 1   c 38
15. a -20   b 21   c -5
    d 4   e -36   f -15
    g 0   h -48   i 15
    j 26
16. a 25°C   b -160 metres
17. a M(-4, -3), N(4, 4), P(5, -2), Q(-1 ,-4),
       R(-4, 4), S(-3, 0), T(2, 2), V(1, -2)
18. a see diagram
    b D(3, -2)
    c A'(-1, 0), B'(-3, -4), C'(1, -2), D'(3, 2)
19. a 0·2, $\frac{1}{5}$ b 0·05, $\frac{1}{20}$

    c 0·36, $\frac{9}{25}$ d 0·75, $\frac{3}{4}$

    e 0·666..., $\frac{2}{3}$ f 0·005, $\frac{1}{200}$

20. a 35%   b 4%   c 70%

    d 27·5%   e 150%   f 33$\frac{1}{3}$ %

21. a £48   b £24
    c £3000   d $1200
22. £180
23. a £57·80   b 620kg   c £10·66
    d £66   e €4730   f £4·20
    g £900
24. a (i) £1914·75 (ii) £22977

    b 78 sheep
25. a 2d   b p²   c 32c
    d 5x + 4y   e t³   f 35ab³
    g 5m   h 12n
26. a 19   b 20   c -40
    d 48   e 2   f 2
    g 10   h 4
27. a 5x + 15y   b 3m2 - 15m
    c -4h + 12   d -10q + 2q²
28. a 5x   b 12b - 12   c 3d - 4
    d 12x - 6   e t + 3   f 4g - 4
29. a 13·4   b 6
30. a P = 4a + 2b + c
    b 67   c 15
31. a 64 cm²   b 66 cm²   c 210 mm²
    a 1260 mm²   b 336 cm²   c 216 cm²
32. a 32 cm   b 35 cm   c 72 mm
    d 154 mm   e 100 cm   f 64 cm
33. a 125 cm²   b 270 cm²   c 49·5 cm²
34. a $\frac{2}{10}, \frac{3}{15}$ b $\frac{6}{22}, \frac{9}{33}$

35. a $\frac{3}{4}$ b $\frac{7}{12}$

    c $1\frac{2}{15}$ d $\frac{23}{30}$

36. a $\frac{11}{5}$ b $\frac{29}{6}$

37. a $1\frac{1}{6}$ b $5\frac{3}{5}$

38. a $7\frac{4}{5}$ b $4\frac{3}{4}$ c $3\frac{11}{12}$

    d $3\frac{5}{8}$ e $4\frac{7}{20}$ f $3\frac{11}{12}$

    g $2\frac{17}{30}$ h $4\frac{5}{8}$

39. $2\frac{5}{12}$ litres
40. a 18·84 cm   b 47·1 cm
41. 12 inches
42. 30 cm
43. a 89·25 cm   b 62·13 mm   c 26·42 m
44. a 3850 mm²   b 56·7 cm²   c 2·54 m²
45. a 56·5 cm²   b 44·2 cm²   c 578 cm²
46. 27 : 18 = 3 : 2
47. a 2 : 3   b 4 : 3   c 1 : 3
    d 3 : 4   e 2 : 3   f 17 : 19
    g 2 : 3   h 5 : 3
48. 40

49. 45
50. 8000 cm³
51. 12·5 cm
52. a 3·5 litres b 0·2 litre c 0·03 litre
53. a 2500 ml   b 3150 ml   c 800 ml
54. a 4200 cm³   b 41·6 m³
55. a 1728000 cm³
    b 1728 litres
56. a 60 km   b 5 hrs   c 350 mph
57. a 200 km   b 40 mph   c 5 hr 15 mi
58. a 9.30   b 15 mins   c 200 mph
    d slowed him down - graph is less steep
    e 120 mph

Answers to Chapter 1 (page 8)

Exercise 1 (Page 8)

1. a 49   b 25   c 36
    d 64   e 49   f 81
    g 100   h 1   i 400
    j 1   k 64   l 1/4
    m 64   n 27   o 125
    p 216   q 1   r 1000
    s -1   t 4   u 1/8
    v 16   w 729   x 1024
2. a 169   b 289   c 441
    d 676   e 1369   f 10000
    g 361   h 90000   i 841
    j 2601   k 1849   l 3364
    m 512   n 1728   o 6859
    p 15625   q -729   r 1/343
    s 1296   t 823543   u 256
    v 59049   w 1000000   x 3200000
3. a 90·25 cm² b 324 cm²
    c 729 cm²   d 148·84 cm²
4. a 41   b 145   c 149
    d 85   e 313   f 38
    g 200   h 841
5. a 1, 3, 5, 7, 9, 11, 13
    b Odd Numbers. 15
    c 17, 39, 201
6. a 390625   b same
7. a 256   b 7776   c 100000
    d 262144   e 729   f 2187
    g 1679616   h 2401   i 1
    j 0   k 128   l 14641
    m 19683   n 244140625
    o 100000000
    p 10000000000
    q 16   r -3125

Exercise 2 (Page 10)

1. a 3 b 5 c 7
   d 8 e 9 f 10
2. a 4 b 1
   c 20 d 30
3. a 20 b 30 c 11
   d 19 e 15 f 16
   g 13 h 17 i 1·2
   j 4·5
4. a 4·12 b 5·10 c 5·83
   d 8·43 e 9·75 f 10·44
   g 13·64 h 24·49 i 27·39
   j 31·62
5. 18 mm
6. a 3 b 4 c 5
   d 10 e 100

Answers to Review Ex 1 (page 12)

1. a £17966 b £2470
   c £29040 d £21112
2. a £496 b £148·80 c £644·80
3. a £5679 b £26599
4. a £728 b £2357
5. £297·50
6. a £5830 b £1722·50

Answers to Chapter 2 (page 13)

Exercise 1 (Page 13)

1. a €558 b 4423·5
   c 5863·5 d 38502
2. a 1512·8 b 11992·6
   c 15896·6 d 104383·2
3. a €15·50 b €1215·20
   c €3224 d €30504
4. a £774·19 b £881·14
   c £138·25 d £23936·17
5. Ellen - £437·10, Kara - £414·19 (✓),
   Louise - £442
6. a £259·68 or £238·71 - $370 cheaper
   b £300 or £350 or £345 - 3909 Rand
7. a £163·23 approx
   b yes - has €360
8. €119·04 approx
9. €744
10. Yes - by £24·36 approx
11. a £483·87 -> $750
    b divide by 13·03 then multiply by 9·83
    c 1966 Yen
12. a €2480 b 4915 Yen c 4278 Rup
13. £5660 approx

Exercise 2 (Page 15)

1. Sm- £2·40/100g, Lge - £2·20/100g (✓)
2. Sm - 35p/50g (✓) Lge - 40p/50g
3. Sm - 22p/25g, Lge - 20p/25g (✓)
4. Sm - £1·20/100ml, Lge - 95p/100 ml(✓)
5. 4 nights - £75/night,
   5 nights - £66/night (✓)
6. 5 nights - £88/night,
   7 nights - £84/night (✓)
7. Small - £13/litre, Big - £11/litre (✓)
8. Small - £2/kg, Medium - £1·80/kg,

Large - £1·60/kg
   a Large b Small
9. 6 - £1·70 each, 16 - £1·70 each,
   24 £1·70 each
   Choose any of them. All same per ball
10. Texico - £1·53/l, Jeet - £1·49/l (✓)
11. Brown - £15·40/m², White - £14/m² (✓)
12. a Jake at £2·40/pie
    b Alan at £1·40/bovril
13. Various

Exercise 3 (Page 17)

1. a PlumbMan - £168,
     PlumbServices - £166 (✓)
   b PlumbMan - £328, (✓),
     PlumbServices - £334
2. a Jay's - £241, Kay's - £211 (✓)
   b Jay's - £349, Kay's - £267
3. BG - £165, Vigin - £165 - Both the same
4. a £145 b £140 - could save £5
5. ElectroFix - £298·50,
   Spark - £286 - Yes
6. a £50 b £30
   c (i) £170 (ii) £350
7. a £40 b £20
   c (i) £140 (ii) £260
8. a/b

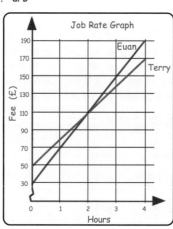

   c Same d >2 e £60
9. Various

Exercise 4 (Page 19)

1. a Yen Rate offers 0·15 Yen/£ more
   b 600 Yen
2. X-Rate - 49100, X-Money - 50300,
   Xpound - 48980
   Will get 1320 Baht more with X-Money
   than Xpound.
3. a Glasgow Bank b £4
4. a Contract is for a year.
   Can change provider easier.
5. a Car Loan b £989 c £301
6. a £119·30
   b NRGEE - £123·00, Power 3 - £120·40
     ScotPow (✓)
   c £1·10 over Power 3
   d Power 3 for gas and ScotPow for
     Electricity

---

   e £111·70 - saved a further £7·60
   f NRGEE Elec + Power 3 Gas - £128·80
     - £17·10 less
7. a Power 3 Elec + SP Gas = £1395·50
   b £1505·60 - 10% = £1355·04.
     She should accept.
8. a Q-Mobile - no need for lots of call
     mins, 5000 texts and only £30 per
     month or possibly Small Talk
   b/c Discussion based on many factors
   d e.g. cost of phone, calls per minute
     over limit, text costs, upgrade
     availability.
9. Various

Exercise 5 (Page 21)

1. a You are borrowing money and if you
     clear your Credit card debt within a
     certain period (might be 1 or 2
     months), you don't pay interest.
     On other hand you are tempted to
     overspend and can easily get into
     debt.
   b Debit Card uses your money. When
     used, funds are taken from your bank
     immediately and this might cause you
     to be overdrawn. You could end up
     paying £20 or £30 evry time in bank
     charges, you use it if you are
     overdrawn. On the other hand, if
     you stay within budget, you are not
     charged interest.
2. a Annual Percentage Rate
   b MNBA has lower APR
   c 3·0% and 2·5%
   d Amix - £36, MBBA - £30
3. APR Int for year with MNBA = £750
   APR for 9 months AMIX = £675 - (✓)
4. a £202·50 b £2430
   c The interest at the end of each
     month is added on to the debt and
     the new interest the following
     month is worked out on this larger
     debt. Also, you are charged an admin
     fee for not paying.
5. £681·50 !!
6. Discussion and presentation

Answers to Review Ex 2 (page 22)

1. a 9·7 b 0·7
2. a 12·52 b 0·90
3. a 1·006 b 0·010
4. a 5000 b 70000
5. a 0·0040 b 5500000
6. a 125000 b 0·0380
7. a 4 b 3 c 6
8. a 10000 b 600000 c 60
   d 300 e 400 f 0·2
9. a 45000 b 50000
10. 4749
11. 2000 miles
12. a 680 b 36900 c 1020000
    d 190 e 12 f 72
13. a 3 b 18 c 13

14. a $(6+2)\times3$　b $18\div(3+6)$
   c $(2+3)\times(5-3)$
15. a 1964, 2000　b €4305　c 34
16. 5263 or 5264
17. £1845
18. a 48　　　　b 500 grams
19. 5 lollies and 15 mice
20. 42p

Answers to Chapter 3 (page 26)

Exercise 1 (Page 26)

1. a 4, 8, 12, 16, 20, 24, 288, 32, 36, 40
   b 3, 6, 9, 12, 15, 18, 21, 24
   c 5, 10, 15, 20, 25, 30, 35, 40, 45
   d 10, 20, 30, 40, 50, 60, 70
2. a 9, 12, 15, 18, 21, 24
   b 30, 36, 42, 48, 54, 60
   c 24, 32, 340, 48, 56, 64, 72
   d 54, 63, 72, 81, 90, 99
3. a 2, 4, 6, 8, 10, 12, 14, 16, 18, 20
   b Even numbers
   c 1, 3, 5, 7, 9, 11, 13, 15, 17, 19
   Odd Numbers
4. a The even numbers from 44 to 56
   b multiples of 5 from 35 to 60
   c multiples of 10 from 120 to 160
   d multiples of 6 from 60 to 90
   e multiples of 9 from 81 to 117
   f multiples of 20 from 60 to 140
   g multiples of 15 from 15 to 75
   h multiples of 50 from 600 to 800
   i multiples of 13 from 39 to 91
   j multiples of 250 from 500 to 1500
5. a 3, 6, 9, 12, 15, 18, 21, ...33, 36
   b 4, 8, 12, 16, 20, 24, ...44, 48
   c 12, 24, 36　　d 12
6. a 4, 8, 12, 16, 20, 24, ...36, 40
   b 6, 12, 18, 24, 30, 36, ...54, 60
   c 12, 24, 36,　　d 12
7. a 5, 10, 15, 20, 25, ... 55, 60
   b 3, 6, 9, 12, 15, 18, ... 42, 45
   c 15, 30, 45　　　　d 15
8. a 10　　　b 6　　　c 36
   d 12　　　e 18　　　f 20
   g 30　　　h 56　　　i 30
   j 72　　　k 36　　　l 44
9. a 30　　　b 24　　　c 40
   d 10　　　e 42
   f 18　　　g 120
10. 120 (about 4 months)
11. 180 seconds or 3 minutes

Exercise 2 (Page 28)

1. 1, 2, 5, 10
2. 1, 2, 4, 7, 14, 28
3. 1, 2, 3, 6, 9, 18
4. 1, 2, 4, 5, 10, 20
5. a 1, 2, 4, 8
   b 1, 2, 3, 4, 6, 8, 12, 24
   c 1, 3, 9, 27
   d 1, 2, 11, 22
   e 1, 2, 3, 5, 6, 10, 15, 30
   f 1, 31

   g 1, 2, 4, 8, 16, 32
   h 1, 2, 5, 10, 25, 50
   i 1, 67
   j 1, 2, 4, 5, 8, 10, 20, 40
   k 1, 3, 5, 9, 15, 45
   l 1, 2, 3, 4, 5, 6, 10, 12, 15, 20, 30, 60
7. a 1, 3, 9　　b 1, 7, 49
   c 1, 2, 3, 4, 6, 9, 12, 18, 36
   d 1, 2, 4　　e 1, 5, 25
   f 1, 2, 4, 8, 16, 32, 64
   g 1, 2, 4, 8, 16
   h 1, 2, 4, 5, 10, 20, 25, 50, 100
   They all have an ODD number of factors
8. a yes　　　b square no's
   c factors match up in pairs except for
   the middle one which only matches
   up with itself.
9. 1 row of 36, 2 rows of 18, 3 rows of 12,
   4 rows of 9, 6 rows of 6 + reverse
10. a 1, 2, 3, 4, 6, 12
   b 1, 2, 3, 6, 9, 18
   c 1, 2, 3, 6　　d 6
11. a 1, 3, 5, 15
   b 1, 2, 4, 5, 10, 20
   c 1, 5　　　d 5
12. a 3　　　b 4　　　c 10
   d 4　　　e 12　　　f 20
   g 17　　　h 6
13. a 1　　　b 1
   c 1　　　d 1
14. a 4　　　b 5
   c 7　　　d 8
15. 1, 2, 3, 4, 5, 6, 8, 9, 10, 12,
   15, 18, 20, 24, 30, 36, 40,
   45, 60, 72, 90, 120, 180, 360
16. 1000
17. Various - Babylonian, Egyptian, Julian...

Exercise 3 (Page 30)

1. 1, 2, 5, 10. It has more than 2 factors
2. 1, 3. It has exactly 2 factors
3. 4. No
4. It has only 1 factor, not 2.
5. a 1, 5 - Yes
   b 1, 2, 4, 8, 16 - No
   c 1, 3, 5, 15 - No
   d 1, 17 - Yes
   e 1, 23 - Yes
   f 1, 3, 9, 27 - No
   g 1, 29 - Yes
   h 1, 5, 7, 35 - No
   i 1, 2, 4, 11, 22, 44 - No
   j 1, 47 - Yes
   k 1, 3, 17, 51 - No
   l 1, 2, 31, 62 - No
6. 20, 42, 33, 36, 40, 49, 50
7. Yes - it has 2 factors, 1 and 2
8. a forever　　b a millisecond - 2

9. a - g

   h 2, 3, 5, 7, 11, 13, 17, 19, 23, 29, 31,
   37, 41, 43, 47, 53, 59, 61, 67, 71, 73,
   79, 83, 89, 97
10. a-e　See Grid
   f 101, 103, 107, 109, 113, 127, 131,
   137, 139, 149, 151, 157, 163, 167,
   173, 179, 181, 191, 193, 197, 199
11. Various results
12. a ends in a 5 ($\div$ 5)
   b even ($\div$ 2)
   c ends in a 0 ($\div$ 10)
   d each dig(it and hence the number
   itself) can be divided by 3
13. Project

Exercise 4 (Page 32)

1. $2 \times 2 \times 3 \times 5$
2. a $3 \times 3 \times 5$
   b $2 \times 2 \times 3 \times 3$
   c $3 \times 3 \times 11$
3. a $2 \times 2 \times 2 \times 2$
   b $2 \times 3 \times 3$
   c $2 \times 2 \times 5$
   d $3 \times 3 \times 3$
   e $2 \times 3 \times 5$
   f $2 \times 3 \times 3 \times 3$
   g $3 \times 3 \times 5$
   h $2 \times 2 \times 2 \times 2 \times 3$
   i $2 \times 2 \times 17$
   j $2 \times 7 \times 7$
   k $2 \times 2 \times 5 \times 5$
   l $2 \times 3 \times 3 \times 3 \times 3$
4. a/b Always get $2 \times 2 \times 3 \times 5$

Answers to Review Ex 3 (page 34)

1. a 0·5, $\frac{1}{2}$　　　b 0·35, $\frac{7}{20}$
   c 0·1, $\frac{1}{10}$　　　d 0·25, $\frac{1}{4}$
   e 0·27, $\frac{27}{100}$　　f 0·125, $\frac{1}{8}$
   g 0·64, $\frac{16}{25}$　　　h 1·00, 1
   i 0·333.., $\frac{1}{3}$　　j 0·02, $\frac{1}{50}$
   k 0·666.., $\frac{2}{3}$　　l 1·5, $1\frac{1}{2}$
2. a 45%　　　b 90%
   c 3%　　　d 80%
   e 70%　　　f 40%
   g 65%　　　h 64%
   i 160%　　　j 0·4%
   k 250%　　　l 1%
3. a £72　　b €32　　c £56
   d 270 l　e $1000　f 75 km
   g €50　　h 2100 ml　i 1620 mm
4. a 640 ml　b 270
   c £241500　d 149·8 cm
5. a £91　　b €815　　c £1260

d £24·31   e £7650   f 5580 mg
g £3·75   h $225
6. a £774   b 87 washes
7. a £26·10   b 144150 km
8. 663
9. Chas - £20572·50
   Tania - £20020
   Donna - £19776
10. £79

Answers to Chapter 4 (page 36)

Exercise 1 (Page 36)

1. a start at 2 and go up by 3
   b start at 7 and go up by 6
   c start at 25 and go down by 5
   d start at 98 and go down by 17
   e start at 3 and times by 3 each time
   f start at 1 and times by 6 ......
   g start at 200 and divide by 2 ....
   h start at 192 and divide by 4 ...
   i start at 1 and times by 4 ....
   j start at $1^1/_2$ and go up by $1/_2$ ...
   k start at $5^3/_4$ and go down by $1/_2$ ...
   l start at 1 and double each time
   m start at 200 and subtract 100 .....
   n start at 108 and divide by 3 ....
   o start at 2 then up 1, down 1, up 1 ....
2. a 17, 20   b 31, 37   c 5, 0
   d 30, 13   e 243, 729 f 1296, 7776
   g 12·5, 6·25 h $3/_4$, $3/_{16}$ i 256, 1024
   j $3^1/_2$, 4   k $3^3/_4$, $3^1/_4$ l 16, 32
   m -200, -300 n $4/_3$, $4/_9$ o 2, 1
3. a 15, 17   b 21, 25   c 18, 16
   d 22, 10   e 27, 81   f 32, 64
   g 12, 6   h 1, 0·1   i 21, 26
   j 13, 21   k 13, 18   l 42, 56
4 1, 4, 9, 16, 25, 36, 49, 64, 81, 100, 121,
   144, 169, 196, 225, 256, 289, 324,
   361, 400
5. a triangle with 1 + 2 + 3 + 4 + 5 circles
   b 4   c 5
   d (i) 66 (ii) 78 (iii) 91
   e 69th number = 68th number + 69
   f 1, 3, 6, 10, 15, 21, 28, 36, 45, 55, 66,
      78, 91, 105, 120, 136, 153, 171, 190
      210
6. a 1
       1 1
       1 2 1
       1 3 3 1
       1 4 6 4 1
       1 5 10 10 5 1
       1 6 15 20 15 6 1
   b start and end each row with 1.
      All other numbers found by adding
      the 2 numbers abpove together
   c 1 7 21 35 35 21 7 1
      1 8 28 56 70 56 28 8 1
      1 9 36 84 126 126 84 36 9 1
      1 10 45 120 210 252 210 120 45 10 1
   d various - natural numbers, triangular

7. a $5^2 - 4^2 = 25 - 16 = 9 = 5 + 4$
      $6^2 - 5^2 = 36 - 25 = 11 = 6 + 5$
      $7^2 - 6^2 = 49 - 36 = 13 = 7 + 6$
      $8^2 - 7^2 = 64 - 49 = 15 = 8 + 7$
   b $11^2 - 10^2 = 121 - 100 = 21 = 11 + 10$
   c $26^2 - 25^2 = 676 - 625 = 51 = 26 + 25$
   d $101^2 - 100^2 = 10201 - 10000 = 201$
      $= 101 + 100$
   e $(n + 1)^2 - n^2 = (n + 1) + n$
8. a 4   b 9   c 16
   d 25   e the square numbers
9. a 15 and 21
   b (i) 100   (ii) 10000
10. a 1, 3, 6, 10
    b triangular numbers
    c $1/_2 n(n + 1)$
    d $1/_2$ of 1000 x 1001 = 500500
11 20 x 19 ÷ 2 = 190
12. 1 + 4 + 9 + 16 + ... + 64 = 204
13. 10 x 7 ÷ 2 = 35
    (A decagon is a 10 sided shape)

Exercise 2 (Page 38)

1. a 12, 16, 20, 24
   b $D = 4 \times C$
   c (i) 80   (ii) 15
2. a 6, 12, 18, 24, 30, etc
   b $B = 6 \times T$
   c 54   d 12
3. a (i) 160, 200, 240   (ii) $P = 40 \times C$
   b (i) 20, 25, 30,   (ii) $A = 5 \times S$
   c (i) 96, 120, 144,   (ii) $H = 24 \times D$
   d (i) 24, 30, 36,   (ii) $C = 6 \times T$
   e (i) 16, 20, 24,   (ii) $L = 4 \times D$
   f (i) 124, 155, 186, (ii) $C = 31 \times R$
   g (i) 48, 60, 72,   (ii) $B = 12 \times C$
   h (i) 264, 330, 396, (ii) $E = 66 \times B$
4. a (i) 8, 10,   (ii) $y = 2 \times x$
      (iii) 40   (iv) 30
   b (i) 12, 15,   (ii) $y = 3 \times x$
      (iii) 60   (iv) 20
5. a 40, 50, 60,   b $r = 3^1/_3 \times S$
   c (i) 200   (ii) 33
6. a (i) 12, 15,   (ii) $y = 3 \times x$
      (iii)(0,0), (1,3) etc (iv) plot points
      (v) line through (0,0) and (5,15)
   b (i) 16, 20,   (ii) $y = 4 \times x$
      (iii)(0,0), (1,4) etc (iv) plot points
      (v) line through (0,0) and (5,20)
   c (i) 20, 25,   (ii) $y = 5 \times x$
      (iii)(0,0), (1,5) etc (iv) plot points
      (v) line through (0,0) and (5,25)
   d (i) 24, 30,   (ii) $y = 6 \times x$
      (iii)(0,0), (1,6) etc (iv) plot points
      (v) line through (0,0) and (5,30)
   e (i) 28, 35,   (ii) $y = 7 \times x$
      (iii)(0,0), (1,7) etc (iv) plot points
      (v) line through (0,0) and (5,35)
   f (i) 4, 5,   (ii) $y = 1/_2$ of x
      (iii)(0,0), (2,1) etc (iv) plot points
      (v) line through (0,0) and (10,5)

7. a (i) -2,.... 3,   (ii) $y = x$
      (iii)(0,0), (1,1) etc (iv) plot points
      (v) line through (-2,-2) and (3,3)
   b (i) -4,.... 6,   (ii) $y = 2 \times x$
      (iii)(0,0), (1,2) etc (iv) plot points
      (v) line through (-2,-4) and (3,6)
   c (i) -6,...., 9,   (ii) $y = 3 \times x$
      (iii)(0,0), (1,3) etc (iv) plot points
      (v) line through (-2,-6) and (3,9)
   d (i) 4, ...-6,   (ii) $y = -2 \times x$
      (iii)(0,0), (1,-2) etc (iv) plot points
      (v) line through (-2,4) and (3, -6)

Exercise 3 (Page 41)

1. a 4, 6, 8, 10, 12,
   b $C = 2 \times T + 2$
   c 42   d 14
2. a 3, 5, 7, 9, 11, 13
   b $L = 2 \times T + 1$
   c 61   d 15
3. a 3, 6, 9, 12, 15, 18, 21
   b $S = 3 \times P - 3$
   c 57   d 30
4. a 3, 5, 7, 9, 11, 13
   b $T = 2 \times S - 1$
   c 49   d 66
5. a £120, £140   b $C = 20 \times D + 20$
   c £300   d 15 days
6. a (i) 6,7,   (ii) $y = x + 2$
   b (i) 9, 11,   (ii) $y = 2x + 1$
   c (i) 11, 13,   (ii) $y = 2x + 3$
   d (i) 9, 10,   (ii) $y = x + 5$
   e (i) 14, 17,   (ii) $y = 3x + 2$
   f (i) 11, 14,   (ii) $y = 3x - 1$
   g (i) -7,3,   (ii) $y = 2x - 3$
   h (i) -10, 6, 10,(ii) $y = 4x - 2$
   i (i) -4, 1,   (ii) $y = x - 2$
   j (i) 4, -6,   (ii) $y = -x$
   k (i) 4·5, 5,   (ii) $y = 0·5x + 2·5$
   l (i) 6·1, 7·3, (ii) $y = 1·2x + 1·3$
7. a (i) 6, 8,   (ii) $y = 2x + 2$
      (iii) (-2, -2), (-1, 0)....
      (iv/v) line through(-2, -2) & (3, 8)
   b (i) 4, 5, 6   (ii) $y = x + 3$
      (iii) (-2, 1), (-1, 2)....
      (iv/v) line through(-2, 1) & (3, 6)
   c (i) 6, 8, 10 (ii) $y = 2x + 2$
      (iii) (-2, 0), (-1, 2)....
      (iv/v) line through(-2, 0) & (3, 10)
   d (i) -5, -3, 5, (ii) $y = 2x - 1$
      (iii) (-2, -5), (-1, -3)....
      (iv/v) line through(-2, -5) & (3, 5)
   e (i) -1, 0, 1, (ii) $y = x - 2$
      (iii) (-2, -4), (-1, -3)....
      (iv/v) line through(-2, -4) & (3, 1)
   f (i) 7, 11,   (ii) $y = 4x - 1$
      (iii) (-2, -9), (-1, -5)....
      (iv/v) line through(-2, -9) & (3, 11)
   g (i) 6, 9, 12 (ii) $y = 3x + 3$
      (iii) (-2, -3), (-1, 0)....
      (iv/v) line through(-2, -3) & (3, 12)
   h (i) -4,...12, 16 (ii) $y = 4x + 4$
      (iii) (-2, -4), (-1, 0)....
      (iv/v) line through(-2, -4) & (3, 16)

i (i) -4, -2, 0 (ii) $y = 2x - 6$
  (iii) (-2, -10), (-1, -8)....
  (iv/v) line through (-2, -10) & (3, 0)
j (i) -5,.. 15, 20 (ii) $y = 5x + 5$
  (iii) (-2, -5), (-1, 0)....
  (iv/v) line through (-2, -5) & (3, 20)
k (i) -2, ..., 6, 8 (ii) $y = x + 2$
  (iii) (-4, -2), (-2, 0)....
  (iv/v) line through (-4, -2) & (6, 8)
l (i) 3, 3,   (ii) $y = 0x + 3$ or $y = 3$
  (iii) (-2, 3), (-1, -3)....
  (iv/v) line through (-2, 3) & (3, 3)
  horizontal line 3 up from origin

Answers to Review Ex 4 (page 46)

1. a -5   b 4   c 6
   d 10   e -5   f 2
   g 0   h 8
2. a 0   b 0   c 90
3. a -20   b 14   c -8
   d 4   e -24   f -24
   g 0   h -24
4. a 2   b 23   c 0
5. a overdrawn by £545
   b +£820
6. 47°
7 a $3p$ b m^2 c $20de$
   d $8a - 2b$ e $4p^3$ f $15t^3$
   g $4x$ h $6s$
8. a 22   b 65   c 49
   d 32   e 3   f 3
   g 16   h 7
9. a $12x + 8$ b $42a - 21b$ c $g^2 + 5g$
   d $12y^2 - 21yz$ e $-6d + 30$ f $-a^2 + 4ab$
   g $-10w + 2w^2$ h $-q^3 - 4q^2r$
10. a $3x + 3$ b $4m - 3$ c $5h + 2$
    d $16g + 3$ e $4b + 3$ f $6d - 3$
11. $10x + 5(x - 1) = 15x - 5$
12. a 6   b 3   c 5
13. 224
14. 20
15. a £288   b £324
16. a. $C = \pi D$
    b 47·1 cm
17. a $P = 4a + 2b + c$
    b 79 cm   c 7·4 mm

Answers to Chapter 5 (page 48)

Exercise 1 (Page 48)

1. a 3   b 10   c 5
   d 0   e 7   f 9
   g 17   h 50   i -3
   j 7   k -13   l 45
   m -8   n 0   o -22
   p -7   q 0   r -38
2. a 8   b 9   c 8
   d 7   e 9   f 1
   g 1·5   h 0   i 0·25
   j 40   k 30   l 3·5
   m 3·25   n 5·8   o $3^2/7$
   p 6·5   q 0·25   r $9^2/3$

---

3. a 3   b 3   c 9
   d 8   e 10   f 1
   g 5   h 1   i 5
   j 6   k 1   l 8
   m 7   n 10   o 8
   p 7·5   q -1   r $2^2/3$
   s -0·5   t 4·5   u 3·25

Exercise 2 (Page 50)

1. a $2x + 1 = 19$ b $7x - 5 = 16$
     $2x = 18$ $7x = 21$
      $x = 9$ $x = 3$
2. a 3   b 8   c 12
   d 7   e 6   f 9
   g 8   h 7·5   i 6
   j 0·5   k 4   l -1
3. a 3   b 4   c 12
   d 1   e 8·5   f 4·5
   g 9   h -6·5   i 13
4. a $3x = x + 20$ b 10
5. a $4x + 9 = 2x + 25$ b 41

Exercise 3 (Page 51)

1. a 3   b 1   c 9
   d 8   e 7   f 1
   g 5   h 4   i 7
   j 1   k 1·5   l -2
2. a 1   b 4   c 1
   d 2   e 7   f 1
   g 5   h 5   i 2·5
   j 7   k 19   l -5
3. a 5   b 4   c 3
   d 6   e 2   f 3
   g 4   h 6   i 10·5
   j 1   k -1   l 4
   m 3   n -10

Exercise 4 (Page 52)

1. a $x + 6 = 14$ b $15x - 100 = 12x - 40$
     $x = 8$ $3x = 60$
                       $x = 20$
2. a 8   b 4   c 24
   d 12   e 15   f 16
   g 6   h $^4/5$ i $1^2/3$
   j $2^1/2$ k $6^1/2$ l $2^2/9$
   m 12   n 20   o $2^2/5$
   p $2^1/6$ q $^2/5$ r $10^4/5$

Exercise 5 (Page 53)

1. a $x > 4$ b $x < 8$ c $x \le 17$
   d $x \ge 5$ e $x \le 12$ f $x \ge 14$
2. a $x < 3$ b $x > 8$ c $x < 6$
   d $x \ge 4$ e $x \le 6$ f $x > 28$
3. a $x < 6$ b $x > 4$ c $x < 3$
   d $x \ge 8$ e $x \le 5$ f $x > 7$
   g $x < 2·5$ h $x \ge 2$ i $x \le 3·5$
   j $x < 28$ k $x \ge 20$ l $x > 10$
   m $x < 7$ n $x \ge 12$ o $x \le 2$
   p $x \le -1$ q $x > 4$ r $x < 21$
   s $x < 3$ t $x > 2·5$ u $x \ge 29$

Answers to Review Ex 5 (page 55)

1. a 20°   b 120°
2. a 35°   b 52°   c 22·5°
   d 35°   e 35°   f 15°
   g 50°   h 50°   i 170°
   j 47°, 133° k 149°, 31° l 54°
   m 60°   n 69°, 42° o 72°, 72°
   p 76°, 80° q 74°, 74°, 106°
   r 42°, 42°, 96°, 138°

Answers to Chapter 6 (page 56)

Exercise 1 (Page 56)

1. a <TPQ   b <FRV & <MVG
   c <EFH & <FGI   d <KLM & <LNO
2. a c   b p   c q
3. a

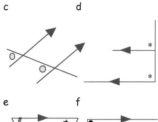

c   d

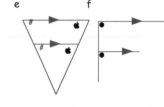

e   f

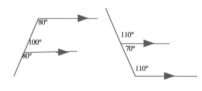

4. a 76°   b 52°   c 68°
   d 105°   e 137°   f 15°, 165°
5. a   b

80° 100° 80°   110° 70° 110°

c

69° 111° 69°

6.

103° 77°
77° 103°
103° 77°

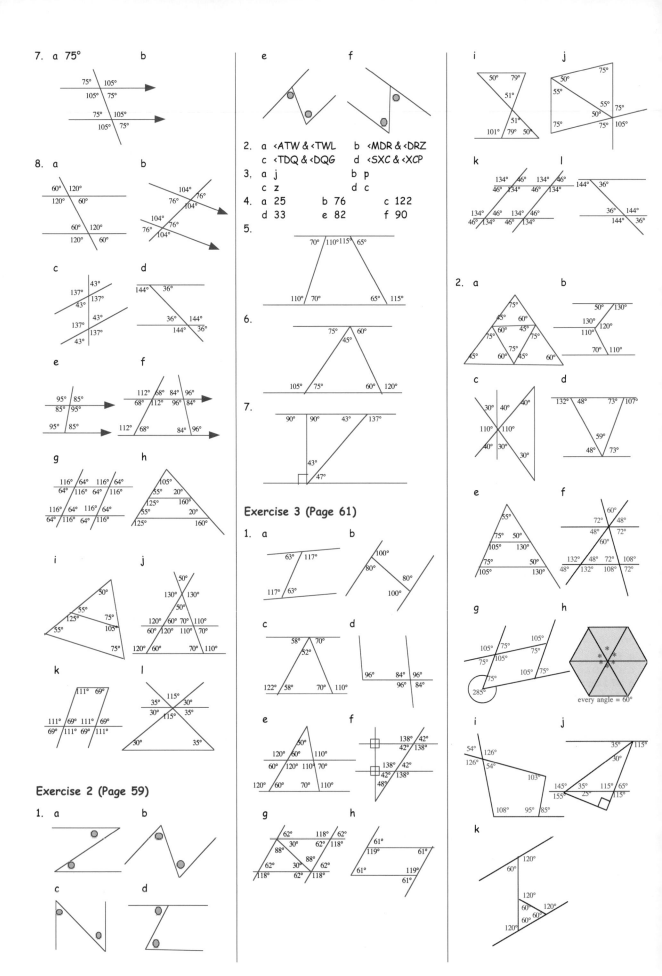

7. a 75°   b

8. a   b

c   d

e   f

g   h

i   j

k   l

Exercise 2 (Page 59)

1. a   b

c   d

e   f

2. a ∠ATW & ∠TWL   b ∠MDR & ∠DRZ
   c ∠TDQ & ∠DQG   d ∠SXC & ∠XCP
3. a j   b p
   c z   d c
4. a 25   b 76   c 122
   d 33   e 82   f 90
5.

6.

7.

Exercise 3 (Page 61)

1. a   b

c   d

e   f

g   h

i   j

k   l

2. a   b

c   d

e   f

g   h

every angle = 60°

i   j

k

Answers to Review Ex 6 (page 64)

1. a Rectangle, A = l x b   42 cm²
   b Triangle,   A = ¹/₂b x h   24 cm²
   c Square,   A = l²   121 mm²
   d Parallelogram A = b x h   456 cm²
   e Kite   A = ¹/₂D x d   1800 mm²
   f Rhombus   A = ¹/₂D x d   2·4 m²
   g Trapezium Sum of 2 triangles 68 cm²
   h Kite   A = ¹/₂D x d   9·6 cm²
   i Triangle,   A = ¹/₂b x h   17 m²
2. a 20·4 m   b 330 mm
3. a 110 cm²   b 174 cm²   c 176 cm²
4. 9000 cm³
5. 2263 cm³
6. a 3·5 l   b 0·27 l   c 0·02 l
7. a 6750 ml   b 2005 ml   c 600 ml
8. a 9000 cm³ b 9 litres
9. 5 cm
10. 7200 cm³
11. 2480 cm³

Answers to Chapter 7 (page 66)

Exercise 1 (Page 66)

1. A Square   B Rhombus
   C Kite   D Parallellogram
   E triangle   F Rectangle
   G Trapezium H Octagon
   I Nonagon   J Undecagon
   K Decagon   L Pentagon
   M Dodecagon N Heptagon
   O Hexagon
2. a 4   b 2   c 3
   d 5   e 9   f 8
   g 9   h 14   i 12
   j 9   k 35   l 4
   m 4   n 2   o 4
   p 7
3. 5 sides - Used to house the American President and his staff

Exercise 2 (Page 68)
1. Check drawing
2. Check drawings
3. Check drawings

Exercise 3 (Page 69)
1. Check drawing
2. Check drawings
3. Check drawings

Exercise 4 (Page 70)
1. Check drawing
2. Check drawings

Exercise 5 (Page 72)
1. Check drawing
2. Check drawing
3. Check drawing
4. Check drawing
5. Check drawing

6. Check drawing
7. Check drawing
8. Check drawings

Answers to Review Ex 7 (page 74)

1. a ²/₆ ,³/₉   b ⁶/₈ ,⁹/₁₂
   c ¹⁰/₁₆, ¹⁵/₂₄ d ⁶/₂₀₀ ,⁹/₃₀₀
2. a ⁴/₅   b ¹/₂   c ⁷/₁₂
   d ¹¹/₃₀   e ³/₅   f ¹/₆
   g 1¹/₁₂   h ³/₁₀   i ⁷/₂₀
   j ⁷/₃₀   k ¹/₅   l ³/₁₆
3. a ⁴⁷/₆₀   b ⁴¹/₆₀   c ³¹/₆₀
4. a ¹¹/₅   b ¹⁵/₈
   c 2³/₇   d 5⁹/₁₀
5. a 2³/₄   b 6²/₃
   c 6³/₅   d 3⁷/₁₁
6. a 2⁵/₆   b 3⁴/₅   c 4²/₃
   d 7⁹/₂₀   e 10¹/₄   f 3¹/₈
   g 5³/₈   h 8⁴/₁₅   i 1⁷/₁₂
   j 1¹⁵/₂₈   k 3⁵/₉   l 2³/₅
7. 2⁵/₆ litres
8. 5¹/₄₀ ounces
9. 3¹/₃ cm

Answers to Chapter 8 (page 75)

Exercise 1 (Page 75)

1. a ³/₅   b ⁵/₁₈   c ⁵/₈
2. a ⁸/₁₅   b ⁷/₁₂   c ⁴/₁₅
   d ¹⁰/₂₁   e ¹/₂   f ¹/₂
   g ¹¹/₂₄   h ¹/₅   i ⁶/₂₅
   j ³/₂₈   k ²⁷/₄₀₀   l ¹¹/₄₈
3. ⁵/₁₆ square metres
4. ³/₁₀
5. ³/₂₀ cubic metres
6. a 4²/₃   b 7¹/₁₂   c 4²/₃
7. a 8¹/₃   b 11¹/₅   c 7⁷/₁₂
   d 4⁵/₇   e 3³/₅   f 8¹/₄
   g 7⁷/₁₀   h 2¹/₁₀   i 6⁵/₁₂
   j 12³/₅   k 38   l 5¹/₅
8. 6 square inches
9. 9³/₈ kg
10. 52¹/₂ kg
11. 16²/₃ seconds
12. ¹/₄ square metre

Exercise 2 (Page 77)

1. a 2¹/₂   b ¹/₄   c ⁹/₁₀
2. a 1⁴/₅   b 2   c ¹/₂

   d ³/₄   e ¹/₂   f ²/₃
   g 1¹/₁₀   h 1¹/₃   i ²⁵/₂₇
   j 1¹¹/₂₄   k 1⁵/₂₇   l 1²/₅
3. a 1¹/₃   b 12
4. a 1⁷/₈   b 3¹/₃   c ⁵/₆
5. a 2⁸/₉   b 1¹/₅   c 1¹/₃
   d 1²/₇   e 1¹³/₃₂   f 6
   g ²⁴/₅₅   h 12¹/₄   i 3¹/₃
   j 7³/₅   k 2²/₅   l 12
6. 6³/₁₀ inches
7. a 2¹/₄ kg   b 2¹³/₁₆ kg
8. 2³/₇ m
9. 5⁵/₉ mins

Exercise 3 (Page 79)

1. a 4⁴/₅   b 5¹/₄
2. a ²⁹/₆   b ⁷²/₇
3. 20
4. a ⁵/₇   b 1¹/₄   c ²/₃
   d 4²/₅   e 2⁴/₁₅   f 6⁵/₆
   g 2⁵/₂₄   h ³/₄
5. a ¹/₆   b ⁸/₁₅   c 7⁷/₁₀
   d 2¹/₂   e 2⁷/₂₄   f 1¹³/₃₂
   g 7¹/₂   h ¹/₉
6. 8³/₄ stones
7. 3¹/₂ kg
8. 15³/₈ kg
9. 5²/₅ cm
10. ¹/₈

Answers to Review Ex 8 (page 81)

1. a A(1, 3), B(3, 3), C(4, 2), D(3, 1),
      E(2, 0), F(1, 1), G(0, 1)
   b G, F & D   c A & F and B & D
   d F & B   e B   f (0, 2)
2.

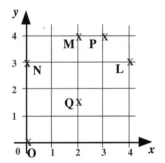

3. a Q(5, -3), R(4, 4), S(0, 3), T(-3, 2),
      U(-1, 0), V(-3, -1), W(-3, -3), X(-1, -2),
      Y(0, -3), Z(2, -1)
   b V & Z and W, Y and Q
   c W & R   d A(2, 2)   e B(-3, -2)

4.

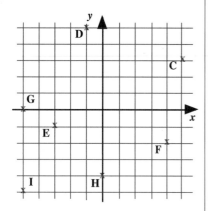

5. a/b/c

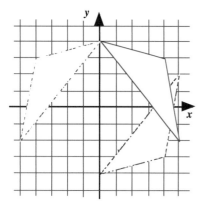

6.

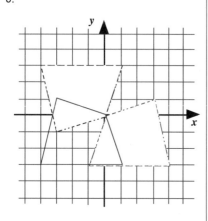

Answers to Chapter 9 (page 82)

Exercise 1 (Page 82)

1. Check drawings
2. Check drawings

Exercise 2 (Page 84)

1. a 34 m   b 12 m
2. a 27 m   b 7·5 m
3. a 190 cm   b 110 cm
4. a 100 cm   b 75 cm   c 125 cm
5. a 216 cm   b 117 cm
6. a 7 cm by 3·5 cm
   b 28 m by 14 m

---

c 6·2 cm × 4 = 24·8 m
7. a 4·5 cm   b 54 km
   c (i) 84 km   (ii) 78 km

Exercise 3 (Page 86)

1. Check drawing
2. Check drawings
3. Check drawing
4. Check drawing
5. a 20 m   b 2 cm by 12 cm
6. a Check drawing
   b 6·5 cm   c 13 m
7. a Check drawing   b 90 cm
8. a 12 m, 3 m   b Check drawing
9. a Check drawing   b 2·7 m
10. Check drawing

Exercise 4 (Page 89)

1. a Check drawing
   b 8·4 cm   c 16·8 m
2. a Check drawing   b 31 m
3. a (i) Check drawing   (ii) 11·6 m
   b (i) Check drawing   (ii) 109 m
   c (i) Check drawing   (ii) 380 m
   d (i) Check drawing   (ii) 1960 m
4. a Check drawing   b 24·6 m
5. a Check drawing   b 70·5 m
6. a Check drawing   b 13·6 km
7. a 1 km   b Check drawing
   c 7·2 km

Exercise 5 (Page 91)

1. a NE   b SW
   c NW   d N
2. a 180°   b 045°   c 270°
   d 135°   e 000°   f 090°
   g 315°   h 225°
3. a 075°   b 315°   c 280°
4. a 045°   b 100°   c 315°
5. a drawing   b drawing
   c drawing   d drawing
6. a Check drawing
   b 6·7 cm   c 67 km
7. a Check drawing
   b 11 cm   c 440 km
8. a Check drawing
   b 10·7 cm   c 53·5 km
9. 250°

Answers to Review Ex 9 (page 95)

1. a 79:103   b 58:79
   c 103:58   d 79:240
2. a 2:3   b 2:1   c 4:1
   d 5:3   d 1:1
3. a 1:100   b 1:60   c 1:6
   d 1:20   e 1:365   f 1:4
   g 1:4   h 14:15
4. a 9:13   b 5:16   c 13:10:9
5. a 45   b 24
6. a 15 m   b 50 cm
7. a Brian - 18, Helen - 9
   b 3 more

Answers to Chapter 10 (page 96)

Exercise 1 (Page 96)

1. Sal - £800, Seth - £1200
2. James - £8000, Pauline - £28000
3. a Peter - £12000, Paul - £33000
   b Anne - £7000, Tom - £5000
   c Gary - £2·15, Dennis - £6·45
   d Pieter - €4080, Helena - €3060
   e Addy - £650000, Steve - £350000
4. a 3:1
   b Ed - £1800, Edie - £600
5. £60000
6. £40
7. a £100 : £200 : £300
   b £100 : £300 : £600
   c $120 : $150 : $330
8. a 10 km   b 5 km   c 35 km
9. 60 mins then 24 mins then 36 mins
10. 120
11. Seb - 10 l, Tim - 5 l, Hen - 20 l
12. small:medium:large = 2:8:10 = 1:4:5

Exercise 2 (Page 98)

1. £1·05
2. a 7p   b £12   c £9
   d 20p   e 20p   f £21
3. 20 tonnes
4. 6 km
5 €1·10 per £
6. 2 kg
7. 1·5 per sec
8. 16 miles per day
9. David - £24, Tim - £22 (✓)

Exercise 3 (Page 99)

1. £56·40
2. £8·10
3. $67·50
4. a 5·4 m³   b 625 times
5. a £4·80   b £20·40
6. a 500   b 3500
   c 30000   d 1800000
7. a no   b no
   c no   d yes
8. a 300   b 50 mins
9. a 50 mins   b 54 lines
10. a £22·50   b 3½ hrs   c 2·8 kg
   d £4·00   e £9·60
11. a £90   b £120

Exercise 4 (Page 101)

1. a 30, 60, 90, 120, 150, 180
   b (1, 30), 2, 60), etc
   c (i) see graph (ii) yes
     (iii) because 0 pears cost 0p
2. a 40, 80, 120, 160, 200, 240
   b (1, 40), (2, 80), etc
   c (i) see graph (ii) yes
3. a 15, 30, 45, 60, 75, 90
   b see graph
   c (i) 120 km   (ii) 97·5 km
4. a (1, 3), 2, 6), (3, 8), (4, 12)

b No. The point (3, 8) doesn't lie on line
5. a 2, 4, 6, 8, 10, 12
   b Yes. All lie on line through (0, 0)
6. c and f
7. see graphs
8. Investigative work.

Answers to Review Ex 10 (page104)

1. a 0·37, $^{37}/_{100}$
   b 0·8, $^4/_5$ c 0·75, $^3/_4$ d 0·025, $^1/_{40}$
2. a 0·125, 12·5%   b 0·727, 72·7%
   c 0·243, 24·3%   d 0·556, 55·6%
3. 0·05, 0·46, 47%, $^{147}/_{300}$, $^1/_2$
4. Eng - 80%, (√), Phy - 70%, Mus - 75%
5. a 28·8 kg   b 12 m   c 5·5 km
   d £217   e 70p   f 0·55 cm
   g 326·4 ml   h £198·40
6. a 24%   b 2064
7. a £31·50   b £78·20
8. a £9600   b 1782

Answers to Chapter 11 (page 105)

Exercise 1 (Page 105)

1. a 1   b 2   c 5
   d 1   e 4   f 1
   g 6   h 4   i 3
   j 1   k 0   l 4
   m 12   n 2   o 0
   p 0
2. see symmetric drawings
3. see symmetric drawings

Exercise 2 (Page 107)

1. a yes   b no   c yes
   d yes   e no   f yes
   g no   h no   i no
   j yes   j yes   l yes
   m yes   n no   o yes
   p no   q yes   r yes
   s yes   t yes
2. a no   b 90°   c $^1/_4$, 4
3. a $^1/_4$, 4   b $^1/_2$, 2   c $^1/_3$
   d $^1/_6$, 6   e $^1/_8$, 8   f $^1/_5$, 5
   g $^1/_6$, 6   h $^1/_3$, 3   i $^1/_4$, 4
   j none , 0   k $^1/_4$, 4   l none , 0
   m $^1/_4$, 4   n $^1/_6$, 6   o $^1/_5$, 5
   p $^1/_8$, 8   q $^1/_8$, 8   r $^1/_7$, 7
   s $^1/_{12}$, 12   t $^1/_3$, 3   u $^1/_8$, 8
   v $^1/_7$, 7   w $^1/_6$, 6   x $^1/_3$, 3
4. See pupil's drawings

Exercise 3 (Page 110)

1. a/b

2.

3.
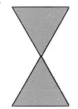

4. a   b   c
   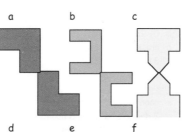
   d   e   f

   g   h   i
   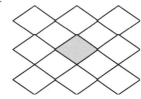

   j   k   l
   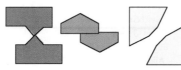

   m   n   o
   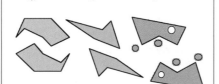

5. Investigation

Exercise 4 (Page 112)

1. a/b

2.
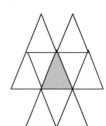

3.
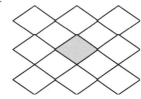

4.
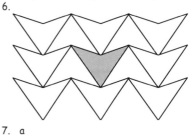

5. a yes   b yes   c yes
   d no   e yes   f yes
   g yes   h yes   i no
   j no   k yes   l yes
   m yes   n yes   o no
   p yes   q yes   r no
   s yes   t yes   u yes
   v yes   w yes   x yes
6.
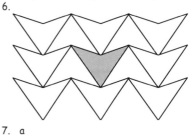

7. a
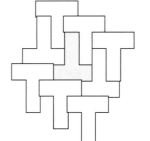

b

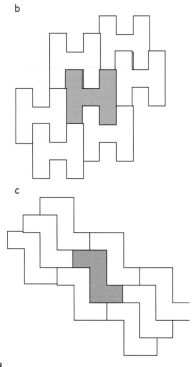

c

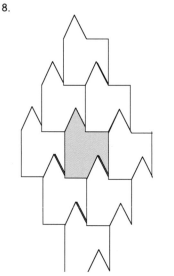

8.

9.

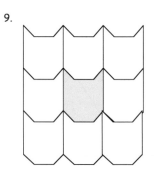

1 a $C = \pi D$ b $A = \pi r^2$
2. a (i) 31·4 cm (ii) 8·79 cm (iii) 25·1 cm
    b (i) 78·5 cm² (ii) 6·15 cm²

(iii) 50·2 cm²
3. 314 cm
4. a 62·8 cm   b 411·2 cm
5. 6 cm
6. a P = 23·42 cm b 38·13 cm²
    b P = 30·71 cm b 37·1 cm²
    c P = 36·84 cm b 84·78 cm²
7. 28·9 m²

Answers to Chapter 12 (page 118)

Exercise 1 (Page 118)

1. Title, scale, even spaces, etc
2. a (i) 25   (ii) 10   (iii) 35   (iv) 25
    b 95   c Wed - zero on graph
3. a 20   b Germany
    c Portugal & Italy - 18
    d Gretna is just over Scottish
       border from England
    e 18 more   f £3440
4. a 1
    b (i) 18   (ii) 38   (iii) 19   (iv) 44
    c chicken   d 19
    e 31   f 132
5. see graph
6. see graph
7. a noon   b 8 am - 9 am
    c 2 degrees d 6 am & noon
    e 3 hours & 2·5 degrees
    f 100 degrees
8. a (i) 8000   (ii) 1200   (iii) 200
    b (i) 1000   (ii) 800   (iii) 300
    c (i) The Tent Store
       (ii) Tents- for-U
       (iii) Same
    d (i) The Tent Store
       (ii) £2500
9. see graph
10. see graph
11. see graph

Answers to Chapter 12 (page 121)

Exercise 2 (Page 121)

1. a & b

	1st 2nd	T1	T2	T3
David Smith	62	81	79
Brian Jones	63	59	91
Bobby Young	71	83	65
Allan Taylor	73	76	79

2. a - e

Customer	length	breadth
Mr Davies	60	80
Mrs White	90	120
Mr Gordon	210	160
Mrs Wylie	75	160
Mr Rivers	130	110
Mrs Jones	80	150

Exercise 3 (Page 122)

1. a & b

	1st 2nd	T1	T2	T3	Ave
David Smith	62	81	79	74
Brian Jones	63	59	91	71
Bobby Young	71	83	65	73
Allan Taylor	73	76	79	76

2. a - c

Customer	length	breadth	Area
Mr Davies	60	80	4800
Mrs White	90	120	10800
Mr Gordon	210	160	33600
Mrs Wylie	75	160	12000
Mr Rivers	130	110	14300
Mrs Jones	80	150	12000

3. a - f

fruit	weight	cost/lb	COST
apples	2·5	£1·52	£3·80
oranges	1·5	£1·80	£2·70
grapes	0·5	£1·68	£0·84
bananas	3	£1·20	£3·60
pears	0	£1·52	£0·00
peaches	0·75	£1·92	£1·44
			£12·38

4. a - e

Name	BH	OH	BR	BP	OP	TP
Fred	40	6	6·50	260·00	58·50	£318·50
Tom	38	4	6·20	235·60	37·20	£272·80
Gina	36	5	4·80	163·20	36·00	£208·80
Alex	39	4	5·10	198·90	30·60	£229·50
Sara	40	2	6·40	256·00	19·20	£275·20
Dave	32	0	5·30	169·60	0·00	£169·60
						£1474·840

5. a - e

Customer	It 1	It 2	It 3	Total
Mr Jones	3·85	9·62	4·75	£18·22
Mrs Paton	6·94	5·73	11·64	£24·31
Mr Wilson	9·85	7·24	1·68	£18·77
				£61·30

6. a - c

Name	...	Pay	Ded	Net
Fred	...	£318·50	£92·40	£226·10
Tom	...	£272·80	£75·30	£197·50
Gina	...	£208·80	£57·79	£151·01
Alex	...	£229·50	£52·72	£176·78
Sara	...	£275·20	£68·77	£206·43
Dave	...	£169·60	£31·42	£138·18

7. various

Exercise 4 (Page 124)

1. a (i) $\frac{3}{10}$ (ii) $\frac{1}{5}$ (iii) $\frac{1}{10}$ (iv) $\frac{2}{5}$
    b Chicken Mayo, Prawn, Tuna, Ham
    c (i) 60   (ii) 30   (iii) 90   (iv) 120
2. a 5%
    b (i) 45° (ii) 25° (iii) 10° (iv) 20°
    c (i) 1000 (ii) 800 (iii) 1800 (iv) 400
3. a $\frac{1}{4}$
    b (i) $\frac{1}{8}$ (ii) $\frac{1}{6}$ (iii) $\frac{1}{12}$ (iv) $\frac{3}{8}$
    c (i) 6   (ii) 3   (iii) 4   (iv) 2
    d 9

4.

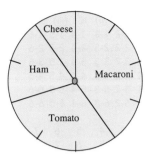

5. a 5%   b

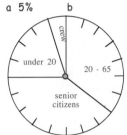

6.

7. a

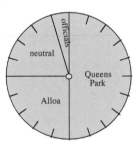

b Supported neither team

Exercise 5 (Page 126)

1. a 180°, 120°, 40°, 20°
   b

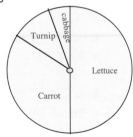

2. a 24°, 168°, 136°, 32°
   b

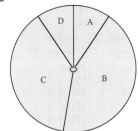

3. a 84°, 48°, 72°, 156°
   b

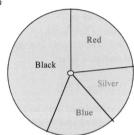

4. a 160°, 120°, 15°, 65°

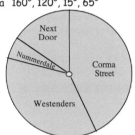

b 190°, 130°, 30°, 10°

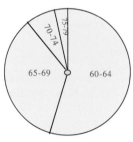

5. a Blackpool - 15, Torquay - 5, York - 6,
   Brighton - 10, Southport - 4
   Angles - 135°, 45°, 54°, 90°, 36°

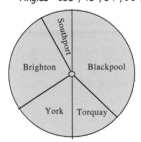

Exercise 6 (Page 128)

1. a R - 8, M = 8
   b R - 17, M = 19
   c R - £22, M = £14
   d R - 27 cm, M = 26 cm

e R - 6·1, M = 7·9
f R - 11·28, M = 8·8

2. £325·89
3. a 5   b 52·5
   c Possibly - the average is 0·5 per
   machine less than claimed
4. a 15   b 7·9
   c See answers
5. a 276   b 69
   c Yes At 272 he would have won
   by 1 shot
6. a R - 0·8, M = 6·55   b 0·35
7. a M - 8, R = 11
   b There are almost double the number
   but sardines were obviously smaller
8. a Norway - £9·12, Scotland - £4·75
   b £4·37

Exercise 7 (Page 130)

1. a R - 7, M = 8
   b R - 44, M = 14
   c R - 4·6, M = 2·2
   d R - 74, M = 80
   e R - 189, M = 122
   f R - $^{11}/_{20}$, M = $^3/_4$

2. a 4   b 16
   c 3·7   d 163
3. a 8·5   b 9·5
   c 6   d 1·25
4. a R - 55
   b Mean - 13, Median - 8, Mode - 4
   c Median
   d Range distorted by the 59 number
   Mode should be middle(ish). Not
   skewed to one end.
5. a R - 23 Kg
   b Mode - 65 Kg, Median - 73 Kg
   c 73 Kg as Median is middle(ish)
6. a Mean - 108, Median - 108,
   Mode - 108
   b 3 jars
7. a Mean - 178 cm, Median - 177 cm,
   Mode - 167 cm
   All chose a different average
   b 167 cm would be least likely
8. a 15 16 16 17 17 18 18 18 18 18 19
   19 19 20 20 21 21 22 22 22 23 23
   23 24 24 24 25 25 29 30
   b Mean - 20·87, Median - 20·5,
   Mode - 18, Range - 15
   c 21 - as close to the mean as possible
   possible lower to encourage pupil more
   higher if the exam was easy
9. £1·36
10. Evelyn is aged 40
11. 17

Exercise 8 (Page 132)

1. a (i) 43 43 43 44 46 47
   (ii) 50 52 56 59
   b 68   c (i) 3   (ii) 0
   d 11   e 22
2. a (i) 6   (ii) 6
   b 10   c 47

d 14 e 21
f none aged in 40's in queue
3. a 2|3 = 23 minutes
b 23 c 8 mins d 23
4. a 0 0 1 6 11 14 14 14 20 21 21
22 25 27 36 39 40 40 43
b 14 c 2
d 19 e 21
5. a 30, 32, 33, 35, 36, 38
b 2| 1 2 7 8 8
3| 0 2 3 5 6 8
4| 3 5 6 7 9
5| 0 2
6| 0 1 2
c Modal - 28 mins, Median - 38 mins
Range - 41 mins
d 2
6. 0| 7 8 8
1| 2 4 6 9 key - 1|2 = £12
2| 0 2 3 5
3| 3
7. 0| 5 8
1| 1 2 4 4 6 7 8
2| 0 3 4 9 key - 2|0 = 20
3| 0 3 5 7
4| 6 6 6 7 7 9
5| 0
8. a 1| 2 5 5 5 8 9 9
2| 1 3 3 5 6 6
3| 0 5 7 7
4| 2 3 8 8
5| 1 4 7 key - 5|1 = 51 secs
6| 0 1 1 1
b 14
c Range - 49 secs
Mode - 61 secs
Median - 32·5 secs
9. (i) a 10| 2 4
11| 1 2 6 7
12| 1 3 6 6 8 8 8
13| 1 2 3
14| 0 0 3
15| 0 1 1 3 6 7
16| 0 2 2 4 5 6 7 8
17| 0 3 5
key - 13|1 = 131
b 73 c 128 d 141·5
(ii) a 0 | 6
1 | 1 1 2 4 8
2 | 3 3 4 4 5 7 8 9
3 | 4 5
4 | 0 2 5 5 7 7 8
5 | 0 1 2 2 2 3 7 8 9
6 | 2 3 5 8
key - 4|4 = 3·4
b 6·2 c 5·2 d 4·35
10. a Male - 13, 16, 19, 19
Female - 12 16 18
b (i) 2 (ii) 2 (iii) 0
c (i) Modal - 42 Median - 35
(i) Modal - 36 Median - 36·5
d 38

11. a 9 |**1**| 8 9
3 3 |**2**| 2 3 7 7 9
7 5 3 2 |**3**| 0
5 |**4**|
b (i) Modal - 23 Median - 32·5
(i) Modal - 27 Median - 25
12. a 9 2 |**13**| 8
8 6 |**14**| 4 5
7 7 6 |**15**| 0 9
4 0 |**16**| 2 7
2 |**17**| 3 4 5
4 1 |**18**| 1 2
b (i) Mode - 157 cms
Median - 157 cms
(i) Mod - no mode
Median - 164·5 cms
c Ashfield have a bigger average since median is larger

Exercise 9 (Page 135)

1. a Biased in favour of keeping open since increased profits will result
b Possibly drunk and obviously in favour of keeping their club open longer
c Obviously they will have been disturbed often by the noise and rowdiness
2. various
3. a discrete b continuous
c continuous d continuous
4. Survey
5. Survey

Answers to Review Ex 12 (page139)

1 a D = S x T b S = D ÷ T c T = D ÷ S
2. 40 words per minute
3. 1360 km
4. 5 hr 36 mins
5. 18 miles per hour
6. a 4·6 hrs b 3 hr 48 m c 108k/hr
7. a 9 am b (i) 30 m (ii) 15 m
c 30 mins d 10 m e 20 mph
f 18 mph

Answers to Chapter 13 (page 140)

Exercise 1 (Page 140)

1. a Rock Paper or scissors
c R-P, R-S, P-S, R-R, P-P, S-S, P-R, S-R, S-P d 1/3 of the time

Exercise 2 (Page 141)

1. a 1/10 b 1/2
c 2/5 d 0
2. a HH, HT, TH, TT b 1/4
c 1/4 d 1/2 e 0
3. a 5 b 1
c 1/4 d no
4. Practical a graph b same no.
c 5 d compare

5. a (i) 3/10 (ii) 1/5 (iii) 1/2 (iv) 0
b (i) 3 (ii) 10 (iii) 50 (iv) 0
6. a 1-1 1-2 1-3 1-4 1-5 1-6
2-1 2-2 2-3 2-4 2-5 2-6
3-1 3-2 3-3 3-4 3-5 3-6
4-1 4-2 4-3 4-4 4-5 4-6
5-1 5-2 5-3 5-4 5-5 5-6
6-1 6-2 6-3 6-4 6-5 6-6
b 36
c 2 3 4 5 6 7
3 4 5 6 7 8
4 5 6 7 8 9
5 6 7 8 9 10
6 7 8 9 10 11
7 8 9 10 11 12
d 7 e 2 or 12 - only one each
f (i) 1/36 (ii) 1/12 (iii) 1/6 (iv) 1/12 (v) 0
g (i) 5/18 (ii) 1/6
7. a 1-1 1-2 1-3 1-4
2-1 2-2 2-3 2-4
3-1 3-2 3-3 3-4
4-1 4-2 4-3 4-4
5-1 5-2 5-3 5-4
6-1 6-2 6-3 6-4
b 2 3 4 5
3 4 5 6
4 5 6 7
5 6 7 8
6 7 8 9
7 8 9 10
c (i) 1/12 (ii) 1/6 (iii) 1/6 (iv) 1/8
d (i) 5/12 (ii) 1/8
8. a 1-1 1-2 1-3 1-4 1-5 1-6 1-7 1-8
2-1 2-2 2-3 2-4 2-5 2-6 2-7 2-8
3-1 3-2 3-3 3-4 3-5 3-6 3-7 3-8
4-1 4-2 4-3 4-4 4-5 4-6 4-7 4-8
5-1 5-2 5-3 5-4 5-5 5-6 5-7 5-8
b 2 3 4 5 6 7 8 9
3 4 5 6 7 8 9 10
4 5 6 7 8 9 10 11
5 6 7 8 9 10 11 12
6 7 8 9 10 11 12 13
c (i) 1/8 (ii) 1/10 (iii) 1/20 (iv) 1/40 (v) 3/40

Exercise 3 (Page 143)

1. 1/3
2. 3/5
3 a 1/6 b 1/6 c 1/2
d 5/6 e 0
4. a 2/5 b 3/5
5. a 1/12 b 1/2 c 1/4
d 1/4 e 5/12
6. a 1/2 a 1/2 c 3/16
d 1/16 e 5/8
7. a 1/9 b 1/3
c 4/9 d 5/9
8. a 1/2 b 1/2 c 1/4
d 1/13 e 1/52 f 3/13
g 5/13 h 1 i 0

9. a $^2/_{15}$ b $^2/_3$ c $^1/_5$

10. a $^{13}/_{25}$ b $^1/_2$

11. a
```
   2   3   4   5   6
   3   4   5   6   7
   4   5   6   7   8
   5   6   7   8   9
   6   7   8   9   10
```
b (i) $^3/_{25}$ (ii) $^1/_{25}$ (iii) 0 (iv) $^1/_5$

12. a HHH HHT HTH HTT
       THH THT TTH TTT

    b 8

    c (i) $^1/_8$ (ii) $^3/_4$ (iii) $^3/_8$ (iv) $^1/_4$

13. 9

14. 20

Exercise 4 (Page 146)

1. $^1/_{12}$

2. $^1/_{13} \times {}^1/_{13} = {}^1/_{169}$

3. $^5/_{16} \times {}^3/_8 = {}^{15}/_{128}$

4. $^1/_7 \times {}^1/_7 = {}^1/_{49}$

5. $^1/_4 \times {}^1/_4 \times {}^1/_4 \times {}^1/_4 = {}^1/_{256}$

6. $^4/_9 \times {}^1/_2 = {}^2/_9$

Exercise 5 (Page 147)

1. $^{13}/_{52} \times {}^{12}/_{51} = {}^1/_{17}$

2. $^4/_{52} \times {}^4/_{51} = {}^4/_{663}$

3. $^4/_{52} \times {}^4/_{51} \times {}^4/_{50} = {}^8/_{16575}$

4. $^4/_{20} \times {}^3/_{19} \times {}^2/_{18} = {}^1/_{285}$

5. $^5/_{25} \times {}^4/_{24} \times {}^3/_{23} = {}^1/_{230}$

6. $^7/_{10} \times {}^6/_9 \times {}^5/_8 \times {}^4/_7 = {}^1/_6$

Answers to Chapter 14 (page 149)

Exercise 1 (Page 149)

1. a 2·416   b 0·008

2. a 9·9   b 4600000

3. 4

4. 400

5. £30

6. a £515   b £35

7. a 12300   b 830

8. a 11   b 16

9. a -14   b 27   c -1
   d -32   e 9   f -1

10. a 24   b 60

11. a 6   b 7

12. 53, 59, 61, 67, 71, 73, 79

13. 2 x 2 x 2 x 7

14. a 25   b 400   c 27
    d 625   e 8   f 30

15. a 0·6   b 0·03

16. a 20%   b 75%

17. a £85   b 70p   c $5

18. £1140

19. 585

20. a $^7/_{12}$ b $6^3/_8$ c $1^{11}/_{15}$

21. a $^{23}/_6$ b $5^1/_4$

22. 5·5 seconds

23. Yes since 8 x 45p = £3·60. 60p discount

24. 75 minutes

25. bottle - 90p/100 ml
    can - 80p/100 ml - better buy

26. £216

27. £1757

28. a 65 mph   b 60 km   c 2 hr 15 m

29. 300 mph

30. a 35 cm²   b 15 cm²

31. C = 314 cm

32. 314 cm²

33. 54000 cm³ = 54 litres

34. 55 cm²

35. a 151, 142   b 30, 42   c 21, 34

36. H = 6d + 9

37. a 3x + 7y   b 20ab

38. a 6m² - 4mn b -12x + 20y

39. 6t + 18s

40. 2

41. a 6   b 8
    c 2   d 44

42. a x > 6   b x ≤ 45

43. a A = 10a + 4b + cd   b 71

44. a 50   b 120   c 110

45. SW

46. 230°

47. 160 m

48. scale factor is 15, 75 cm

49. a P(-1, 0)   b S(3, -2)   c R'(5, 2)

50. a yes   b no   c yes
    d yes   e yes

51. a £160   b £50
    c £35   d £30

52. 76

53. a $^5/_{12}$ b 75

54. $^2/_5$

55. 15

56.